ALL SORTS OF GOOD SUFFICIENT CLOTH

LINEN-MAKING IN NEW ENGLAND
1640-1860

View of a section of "Linen-Making in New England" as installed at the Museum of Our National Heritage, Lexington, Massachusetts. Addis Osborne, exhibit designer.

ALL SORTS OF GOOD SUFFICIENT CLOTH:
LINEN-MAKING IN NEW ENGLAND
1640-1860

MERRIMACK VALLEY TEXTILE MUSEUM
NORTH ANDOVER, MASSACHUSETTS

1980

Catalogue designed by Robert Hauser of Busyhaus and printed by Meriden Gravure in an edition of three thousand. Printed on Mohawk Superfine, bound and smyth sewn by Robert Burlen & Sons. Cover design rubbing of huck weave towel (S.P.N.E.A. 1949.17A) printed on Strathmore Chroma. Typesetting by Mary O'Brien, Studio Composition, using IBM Aldine Roman. Catalogue photographs by Robert Hamel. Frontispiece photo by Steven Burger and Fig. 2 by Benjamin Magro.

CONTENTS

ACKNOWLEDGMENTS

Several years ago, as I examined the antique flax-processing tools and prints of linen-making processes which are in our collection, it occurred to me that the materials deserved to be exhibited. In 1977, when faculty members at Worcester Polytechnic Institute assigned two students to study in the Museum, we were able to begin planning the exhibition. Laurel Wiljanen Neece and Terry Langevin spent a summer exploring with great imagination the collections of New England's museums and historical societies. They concluded that an exciting and important exhibit could be assembled.

When Martha Coons, a National Endowment for the Arts-sponsored intern from Boston University, came to work at the Museum in January, 1978, I assigned to her the task of preparing a lengthy outline for an exhibit of linens and flax-processing tools. Over the course of the next few months she did the necessary research and wrote a formal proposal which was funded by the National Endowment for the Humanities.

The Museum of Our National Heritage, Lexington, Massachusetts, and the New Hampshire Historical Society, Concord, New Hampshire, agreed to present the exhibit in their spacious galleries and to assist us with research and in locating objects. At the Museum of Our National Heritage, Addis Osborne designed the exhibit and supervised its installation, while Barbara Franco gave incisive critical comment on the script at every stage. Marcy Wasilewski advised us about the educational opportunities which the exhibit affords. James Garvin energetically oversaw the project at the New Hampshire Historical Society, where William Copeley guided our researchers through the recesses of the Society's considerable collections of books and local records and Stuart Wallace gave freely of his expertise on the Scotch-Irish. We are extremely grateful to Clement Silvestro, Director of the Museum of Our National Heritage, and to John Page, Director of the New Hampshire Historical Society, for this unusual display of institutional cooperation.

As the project progressed, many professional colleagues and owners of tools and textiles provided crucial help. Jane Nylander of Old Sturbridge Village, Anne Farnam, Bettina Norton and Dean Lahikainen

1

of the Essex Institute, Melvin Watts of the Currier Galley of Art, Richard Nylander and Brock Jobe of the Society for the Preservation of New England Antiquities, Virginia Plisko of the Manchester Historic Association, Mary Flinn and Martha Larson of the North Andover Historical Society, and Marilyn Ham of the Londonderry Historical Society encouraged us to use the collections in their institutions. Bessie Swain, Edward Franquemont, Mr. and Mrs. Joseph Marcus and Mr. and Mrs. J. Kenrick Butler offered items from their private collections. Without the help of Jane Nylander and Caroline Sloat, also of Old Sturbridge Village, our historical grasp of the subject would have been much sketchier. Each suggested several new sources to Martha Coons and generously provided access to her own notes on some obscure manuscripts and local records.

Since November, 1978, the production of the exhibit and catalogue have occupied a large part of my own time and required significant contributions by several members of my staff. Martha Coons, as Assistant Project Director, researched and worked full-time on both exhibit and catalogue. Helena Wright selected the prints and photographic reproductions. Robert Hamel took all of the photographs not otherwise credited and produced the enlargements for the catalogue. Paul Hudon designed the education programs which accompany the exhibit. Emily Van Hazinga, this year's graduate intern from Boston University, offered on many occasions constructive criticisms, historical insights or bits of linen lore to illuminate our project. Michael Bogle and Elizabeth Lahikainen cleaned and installed the textiles. Robert Hauser prepared the tools for display. Finally, Katherine Koob logged endless hours with Martha Coons, making her way through stacks of towels and ticking, shuffling many drafts of script and text, and preventing loose threads from allowing the entire project to unravel.

Throughout the project, the support and encouragement of former and current staff members at the Endowment were critical; we especially want to thank Glenn Long, Cheryl McClenney, and Andrea Anderson.

Thomas W. Leavitt
Director

ALL SORTS OF GOOD SUFFICIENT CLOTH

LINEN-MAKING IN NEW ENGLAND
1640-1860

Fig. 1
Flax wheel made for Captain James Anderson of Londonderry, N.H. 34 x 24 x 41″
Privately owned.

In the fabric of the British society from which America's first settlers migrated, handspun linen threads made up the warp and weft. Every household relied on linen for clothing, bedding and many other uses from book bindings to ships' sails. When the farmers and villagers of England, Ireland and Scotland left their homelands to settle in the New England wilderness, they brought with them both a taste for linen and the skills to make it. The development of an American linen industry in the seventeenth and eighteenth centuries is a little-studied but central episode in this country's early economic and cultural history. With the introduction of machine-made cotton cloth in the early nineteenth century, domestic linen-making nearly disappeared, accompanied by social and economic changes which represent in microcosm the larger consequences of the Industrial Revolution in America.

European men and women had been making linen at least since the fourteenth century, using a series of processes to extract from the flax stalk fibers which were spun into yarn, woven, and bleached in the sun. Although these processes — retting, braking, scutching (or swingling) and hackling — changed little through the preindustrial period, a few improvements did occur while New England was being settled. During the seventeenth century the Dutch perfected the efficient Saxony or "low Irish" wheel, which was capable of continuous spinning (fig. 1). The bleaching process was shortened with the invention in the 1760s of a bleach compound of chlorine in lime. Meanwhile, the development of trade made larger and better quality supplies of flax seed and raw flax available, encouraging the development of linen industries in England, Scotland, Ireland, Italy, Belgium, Spain and Sweden.[1]

In each of these countries, the linen industry was based in the farm household, where most families made linen for their own use. As markets and trade routes developed, more home-made linens were sold in the cities or exported. At first, a single family would grow and process the flax as well as spin and weave the linen. The product would be sold at the large fairs where merchants transacted business. Increasingly, a division of labor occurred. A farmer would set up a weaving shop, invest in looms, hire one or two other weavers, and take in yarn spun in local households. Another farmer would set up a bleach green to whiten the linen produced in the surrounding area.

Flax and yarn, first sold directly by the farm families who produced them, were soon handled by entrepreneurs who imported the raw material from fertile countries like Russia, or bought up yarn to sell to the weavers. Linen merchants built fortunes by selling the product of the weavers' looms. Though the farm household remained the basic unit of production until later in the eighteenth century, the industry expanded on many levels. Merchants opened more markets for flax, yarn and cloth (fig. 2), weavers perfected a greater variety of cloths in wider and better grades, and linens of all kinds were exported around the globe (fig. 3).[2]

Many of the immigrants who populated New England between 1620 and 1750 had learned the techniques of linen-making in the towns and countryside of England. The settlers were preoccupied with obtaining food and shelter and with creating rudimentary economic and political institutions. They were not prepared immediately to recreate the thriving linen industry of Europe. Nevertheless, the colonial governments began to press settlers to manufacture more of their own textiles as early as 1640. In that year, the Massachusetts General Court directed towns to "inquire what seeds are necessary for growing flax, to ascertain what persons are skillful in braking, use of wheels, weaving, etc." In 1656, Massachusetts declared the select-men in each community responsible for teaching girls and boys to spin, requiring each spinner to produce three pounds of linen, cotton or woolen yarn each week for thirty weeks of the year. Both Massachusetts and Connecticut offered a bounty for linen made in the country in 1640; Massachusetts repeated the offer in 1709, 1722, and 1753.[3]

In Boston, community leaders organized spinning schools and spinning contests starting early in the eighteenth century to ensure that the skills of spinning and weaving would not die out among a new generation of English colonists. In 1720, the Boston town meeting called for a spinning school to be established on Longacre Street. Although historians doubt that the building was erected, a resident later recalled that "Great show and parade were exhibited on the Common at [the spinning school's] commencement. Spinning-wheels were then the hobby-horses of the Publick. The females of the Town, rich and poor, appeared on the Common, with their wheels and vied with each other in the dexterity of using them."

6

Fig. 2
Portrait of linen merchant. Privately owned.

A financial crisis in the late 1740s renewed the need for a school, as "the Number of Poor is greatly increased, and the Burden of supporting them lies heavy on many of the Towns within the Province, and many Persons, especially Women and Children, are destitute of Employment." Prominent Bostonians founded the Society for Encouraging Industry and Employing the Poor in 1751, raising private subscriptions. Two years later, they secured public support for a linen "manufactory" and spinning school. A tax on carriages and chaises levied by the General Court was used to purchase a new building on Tremont Street and to pay tuition for one pupil from each town in the state. At the gala opening of the new establishment, "Near 300 spinsters, some of them 7 or 8 years old and several of them Daughters of the best Families among us," joined local weavers in a demonstration on the Common.[4]

Although it is difficult to assess how effective these legal incentives and spinning schools were, local records do show that as the colonies grew and prospered, families were starting to manufacture some of their own linen cloth. A Bostonian writing in 1642 thanked Divine Providence for taking a part "in prospering hempe and flaxe so well that it is frequently sowne, spun, and woven into linnen cloath." As early as the 1670s, probate inventories recorded in Suffolk County, Massachusetts, reveal that rural householders owned flax brakes, tow combs, and "linnen wheels," as well as supplies of raw flax or linen "yarne at weaving." John Weld of Roxbury, who died in 1691, was typical: he left a "parcell of linnen yarne, course Table Cloths, 8 towels, woollen and linnen wheels and Cards, and tow yarne." Inventories from Providence, Rhode Island between 1716 and 1726 also include "flax in sheaf," hatchels (hackles), linen wheels, and tow and linen cloth.[5]

In many cases, colonists combined a linen warp with a cotton weft: "and so, with cotton wooll (which we have at very reasonable rates from the Islands) and our linnen yarne, we can make dimitees and fustians for our summer clothing."[6] When he died in 1688, John Richards of Dedham left a "cotton wheele" as well as a "woolen wheele and Cards," suggesting that he used a modified flax wheel or a second wool wheel for the purpose. No doubt the colonists' decisions to use cotton or linen thread depended on the balance in each

8

Fig 3
"Perspective View of the
Linen Hall in Dublin, with
the Boxes and Bales of Linen
ready for Exportation, The
Emblems of their Industry . . . ."
William Hincks, Plate XII
(London: 1783) Engraving.

An Act for Continuing the Liberty of Exporting *Irish* Linen Cloth to the *British* Plantations in *America* Duty-free; And for the more effectual Discovery of and Prosecuting such as shall unlawfully Export Wooll and Woollen Manufactures from *Ireland*; And for Relief of *John Fletcher*, in respect of the Duty by him paid for a Quantity of Salt lost in the Exportation for *Ireland*.

Hereas by an Act passed in the Third and Fourth Years of the Reign of Her late Majesty Queen Anne, Intituled, An Act to Permit the Exportation of *Irish* Linen Cloth to the Plantations, and to Prohibit the Importation of *Scots* Linen into *Ireland*; It was Enacted for the Support of the Protestant Interest of Ireland, and for the Encouragement of the Linen Manufactur of that Kingdom, That it should and might be lawful to Export from Ireland, directly to the British Plantations, all sorts of White and Brown Linen Cloths, being the proper Manufacture of the said Kingdom, under certain Restrictions and Conditions in the said Act mentioned, for the Term of Eleven Years; which Act hath been since continued for One Year, and to the End of this present Session of Parliament, by an Act passed in the First Year of the Reign of His present Majesty King George, Intituled, An Act for Continuing several Laws therein mentioned, relating to Coals, Hemp, and

Qqqqqq

Fig. 4

[3 Geo. I] *An Act for Continuing the Liberty of Exporting* Irish *Linen Cloth to the* British *Plantations in* America *Duty-free* . . . (London: 1717)

locality between the cost of cotton shipped in from the West Indies and the labor involved in processing flax into linen. In areas with good transportation and trade, a variety of both cotton and linen cloths were available by mid-eighteenth century. Samuel Gaylord, Jr., of Hadley, Massachusetts, a weaver who worked between 1745 and 1772, offered for sale tow cloth, fine linen, cotton and linen, sacking, linsey-woolsey, checked linen, fine check, bedtick, diaper, diamond table linen, birdseye, fine crash, and coverlids.[7]

Early in the region's history, then, the settlers of New England made some of their own cloth, but during the colonial period they relied heavily on textiles imported from Europe. Merchants imported large selections of linen fabrics into the port cities, making them available in retail stores to city dwellers and, to a lesser extent, to rural residents living where trade was well-developed. For instance, in Boston in 1735, Henry Caswell sold "garlix and Bag Hollands, Kentins, Cambricks & Lawns, Dantzick and Russia Linnens, brown and white Oznabrigs, Hollands, Irish and New England Duck, Dowlas" and other fabrics. Besides "homespun cloth," John Gilman sold "Galick" and oznabrig at his general store in Exeter, New Hampshire in the 1740s. Robert Traill of Portsmouth, New Hampshire, imported these fabrics in 1757: canvas of most sorts, oznaburgs, ticklinburgs, linnen checks, buckrams, damasks, linnens, hollands, cambricks, lawns, and Prussia and Russia linnens.[8]

Independently, but at about the same time that the English immigrants were building up a small domestic linen industry, another group of immigrants — the Scotch-Irish — developed their own linen manufacture following the tradition of their ethnic community in northern Ireland (Ulster). Several factors had combined to make both the art and business of linen-making in northern Ireland among the most highly developed in Europe. First, Ulster's damp climate and rich soil were well adapted to flax. Second, a zealous Earl of Strafford, Thomas Wentworth, introduced the Saxony wheel into the province in 1638, then vigorously enforced laws requiring its use. Third, the British Parliament, which governed Ireland, passed laws encouraging the Irish linen industry (fig. 4). Beginning in 1698, a series of strict acts served to repress Irish woolenmaking, and so to protect the English woolen industry, but at the same time opened

11

unrestricted trade for Irish linens. A Linen Board to regulate the industry was set up in 1711, skilled workmen were brought in from Holland, France, and elsewhere, and spinning schools were set up.[9]

Furthermore, since the first quarter of the seventeenth century, the Irish linen industry had benefited from the skills of Scotch Presbyterians, who had migrated to Northern Ireland in search of cheap land. Wishing to build up the Protestant population, the government offered these migrants large, fertile estates at low rent, which the Scots used to develop their clothmaking industry. After 1685 they were joined in the province by another group of Protestants with a spinning and weaving tradition, the French Huguenots, who were fleeing persecution in the wake of the repeal of the Edict of Nantes. Each group contributed their skills to the development of a strong Ulster linen industry.[10]

By 1710 the Ulster Scots found conditions deteriorating badly. Anglican rulers demanded tithes and forbade Presbyterians from holding public office. The linen business suffered periodic depressions, and on the once-inexpensive estates, landlords began to charge exorbitant "rack rents." Many of the Scotch-Irish responded by moving once again, this time to New England. In 1718, one hundred and twenty Scotch-Irish families sailed for Boston; some settled there, some moved on to Worcester, Massachusetts, and sixteen families founded the town of Nutfield, New Hampshire, which they renamed Londonderry in 1722 (fig. 5). Some ninety other families had joined them by late 1719, and the community quickly became the largest Scotch-Irish settlement in New England. Over the next fifty years, Londonderry residents scattered into over twenty new towns in New Hampshire, Maine, New York and other states. Into such "second generation" towns as Peterborough, Bedford, and Candia, New Hampshire, Belfast, Maine, and Londonderry, Vermont, these settlers brought their skills in the making of fine linen.[11]

Before the eighteenth century had ended, local historians began to boast of the importance of the Londonderry linen industry, usually exaggerating its stature with partisan pride. Numerous writers credit these Scotch-Irish immigrants with the introduction of linen-making into America. Jeremy Belknap, New Hampshire's first historian, wrote in 1791,

Fig. 5
An Accurate Map of His Majesty's Province of New Hampshire in New England.
Joseph Blanchard and Samuel Langdon (Portsmouth, N.H.: 1761) Engraving.
New Hampshire Historical Society.

These people brought with them the necessary materials for the manufacture of linen; and their spinning wheels, turned by the foot, were a novelty in the country. They also introduced the culture of potatoes, which were first planted in the garden of Nathaniel Waller of Andover.[12]

According to Reverend Edward Parker, the mid-nineteenth century historian of Londonderry,

These settlers . . . introduced the art of manufacturing linen of superior quality, the materials for which they brought with them . . . The spinning wheel turned by the foot, which came into general use, they first brought into the country, and it proved of essential service to the community.[13]

Drake's *History of Boston* (1856) states that a number of the Scotch-Irish settled in Boston while their companions moved on to Londonderry, and that these settlers introduced the linen wheel. Gordon Woodbury cited and elaborated upon Drake's story in 1905, stating that when the Scotch-Irish arrived in Boston their linen wheels attracted so much attention that the women were induced to set up an exhibition on Boston Common. Writing about Windham, New Hampshire, which was settled by natives of Londonderry, Leonard Morrison recorded that "in 1722, Irish potatoes and manufactured linen goods from an American foot wheel, were on exhibition at a Derry [New Hampshire] fair, for the first time in America."[14]

Partisan local historians surely claim too much for the Scotch-Irish when they credit them with introducing linen-making into America, since inventory records show clearly that English immigrants were using linen wheels and other flax tools as early as the 1670s in Massachusetts. The repeated reference to the potato and the linen wheel in the same literary breath suggests that nineteenth- and twentieth-century historians relied heavily on Belknap's colorful, but undocumented account.

The town and provincial records of early New Hampshire, however, do show that Londonderry linens attracted imitators. As early as 1728, the town appointed James Alexander "for sealing of weights, measures, leather and all sorts of Good sufficient linen Cloth that are made in this town for this Enschewing Year." The matter came before the House of Representatives of New Hampshire in 1731. That body resolved:

> Whereas there are great frauds and deceit practiced by persons travelling in this Province by selling of Foreign Linnens under pretence they were made at Londonderry, in this Province, which tends to the Damage of those who really make and sell the Linen in Londonderry, &c, for prevention of which and for encouraging the manufacturing of Linen in said Town, *voted*, That an Act be drawn up authorizing the said Town to make choice of a suitable person to seal all such linen as shall be made in the said Town, and to have a Seal with the name of the Town engraved on it, and authority to such sealer (if suspect 'twas not made in the Town) to administer an oath to the persons that bring linen to be sealed, that it was *bona fide* made in said Town.

Apparently, Londonderry let the matter slide for many years, or perhaps residents chose an inspector informally. There is no record that the town meeting elected any inspectors of linen in the 1730s, although they did vote for sealers of leather starting in 1740. In 1748, however, a notice for a town meeting again raised the issue:

> [There will be a town meeting] To see if the town will Chuse a proper and fitt person or persons to survay and Inspect the linens and hollands made in this town for seal that so the Credate of our Manefactors may be keept up and the bayers and purchers of our linens may Not be Imposed upon with foreign and outlandish Linens in the name of ours or any other Method that may be thought proper and neceray for that End as may be agreed upon.

For two years following that action, Londonderry citizens elected sealers of linen, before again dropping the office from their slate of offices.[15]

European travelers verify that by late in the eighteenth century, Londonderry's reputation as a linen center was well-established. In 1750, James Birkit wrote, "This province [New Hampshire] also produced . . . Exceeding good flax of which the Irish Settled at Londonderry Make very good Cloth & fine Ounce thread, Some of the Cloth I see which was choise good Shirting Linnen and I am informed this little town increases very much."

15

George Grieve observed in 1787,

> Flax has become a very great and profitable article of culti-
> vation in the Middle and Eastern States, the principal culti-
> vators are settlers from the north of Ireland, who know the
> value of it in their own country. In Massachusetts [actually
> New Hampshire] there is a very considerable and thriving
> settlement, called Londonderry, peopled entirely by
> emigrants from that city, where they apply themselves
> particularly to the growth of flax.[16]

From scattered personal and public records and from the few extant
Londonderry textiles, it is possible to reconstruct the outlines of the
Scotch-Irish linen industry. Although the social organization of linen-
making tasks may have differed slightly among other ethnic communities, the example of the Scotch-Irish in the Londonderry area
allows close examination of colonial household industry in well-
developed form. The demands of growing flax and making linen provided each member of the household with tasks traditionally allotted
by age and sex, and tied the community together in mutual depend-
ence. Family members and neighbors cooperated to complete tasks
as the seasons required. Field labor, braking, and swingling were
heavy, outdoor tasks usually, but not always performed by men,
under financial arrangements which were often casual. On the
Matthew Patten farm in Bedford, New Hampshire, "Sarah Currier
helped us to pull [harvest] flax" for three days in July 1766, and in
February "Alexr came and swingled flax for me and Charles Black
swingled on his acct." John Campbell, a Windham, New Hampshire,
farmer, recorded the following schedule:

March hath 31 Dayes 1796

24 thrash 12 sook oats and Clean 10 Bushells
25 swingle 19 1/4 of falax John Cochran Breaked 19 Bundles
26 swingle 20 1/2 pound flax John Cochran Broke 20 Bundles
   Spend /3
27 goe to Town Meeting Spend 1/4d agumment of agumment
28 Thrash 14 1/2 sooks of oats Jam Henry hear Braked flax
29 swingle 15 1/4 pounds of flax John Cochran Breade
   15 Bundles
31 go to McGaws after stears Spend 1/3 d

16

Apriel Hath 30 Dayes 1796

> 1st Breake flax for Jamison Henry Goe to George Davidsons
>   to frolic
> 2 Brake flax to Ditto finish Medow hay Begin on Inglish hay
> 3 Sunday Stay at home spring like wether Loss goos Last night
> 4 Break flax for Jam Henry foornoon and for myself
>   in afternoon
>   Break 18 Bundles Jamison swingle 14 for mee Spend 14d1/2
>   On moor Dye

Typically responsible for the indoor tasks of hackling and spinning, women employed an array of equipment described in their husbands' probate inventories. The John McConnaghy home in Bedford, for instance, contained "3 foot wheeles, 2 clock reels, 18 spindle of linen yarn, 2 hatchels, one great wheel," while the David Craigs of Londonderry kept "2 flax combs, one little new spinning wheel, one old spinning wheel and reel, one great woolen wheel, two yards and a quarter of linnen, and coarse tow yarn." As wives and daughters kept busy with spinning in their own homes, unmarried women or widows sometimes came into other households to spin for pay. Again, accounts were kept loosely in the small communities: "I paid Mary Houston 21 s/ old Tenor that I owed her for spinning she did here some years ago," wrote Patten in 1761. In 1765, "I paid Elizabeth Patten 1-7-6 Bay Old Tenor Toward her Spining for us last faul or Summer."[18]

In contrast to the flax-dressers and spinners at work in every family, a relatively small number of weavers in the town produced cloth from the yarn spun in the surrounding households. Some weaving was of a routine nature for home use, while other cloth was more elaborate and contributed to Londonderry's regional reputation. The distinction between home and professional weaving is not a clear one, however. Although most women probably produced mainly for the home, they often earned money by weaving for others. Matthew Patten wrote in 1765, "I went to Mr Marstins and got 12 3/4 yards of Cloath his wife wove for us and I paid her 4-19-0 for weaving it," and in 1766, "Susannah brot home 13 yds of tow cloth that Capt Barrows wife wove for us." Men performed a similar service locally; as Patten noted in 1766, "I carried some linen yearn to David McClearys to be Wove."[19]

Using yarn spun in their own and neighbors' households, a few highly accomplished professional weavers, male and female, developed their craft into a business and an art. In the inventory of Robert Wilson of Londonderry, who died in 1769, "fine linen cloth, striped and checked cloth, cambrick, and indigo" appear along with the common wool and flax, "spools swifts a reel and flax combs." Robert Boyes of Londonderry left "tow linnen and cotton yarn, 6 pounds of cotton, 4 yds of check, 12 yds of table linen, fine hatchels and ditto course, and baby linnen" in 1768. In 1729 and again in 1736, John McMurphy sold the town lengths of linen to be used as gifts for the governor, while according to Parker, John Montgomery received from Congress 4 pounds and a diamond ring, as a premium for linen woven for George Washington's army officers. Such weavers were capable of weaving exceptionally elaborate patterns; a surviving fragment of the altarcloth used in the Londonderry Presbyterian church is a damask weave, made up of a three-block, five-harness satin pattern (fig. 6). A tablecloth associated with the Ela family is an example of a twill diaper weave with a two-block, four-harness twill pattern (fig. 7). Requiring looms of multiple harnesses — eight for the twill and fifteen for the damask — these textiles were the work of master weavers.[20]

If flax grown and spun on Scotch-Irish farms and cloth woven on sophisticated looms were the basis of the Londonderry linen industry, marketing skills were responsible for its development beyond the local area. Little concrete evidence of merchant activity survives, but Parker describes the Pinkerton brothers, James and John, who built fortunes vending home-manufactured linen. A British official writing in 1768 described the linen industry in New Hampshire, "This manufacture finds a ready Sale, tho' dearer than imported Linnen: from its superior Strength and goodness." One element in the successful merchandising formula was the Londonderry fairs, where "all the country flocked to a focus, bringing with them the products of their industry, and the superfluity of their household goods, to be exchanged, bartered, and sold." Local lore testifies that the Londonderry fair, begun soon after the Scotch-Irish arrived, was the first agricultural fair in the country. Modeled after the fairs of Ireland, events included horseracing, foot races, wrestling, dancing and even weddings as well as the exchange of linen and agricultural products.

Fig. 6
Communion tablecloth, fragment. Warp: undyed single Z-twist linen, 56 per inch; weft: undyed single Z-twist linen, 42 per inch; edges: 1 selvage, 3 hemmed; size: 6 1/2 x 6″ Londonderry (N.H.) Historical Society.

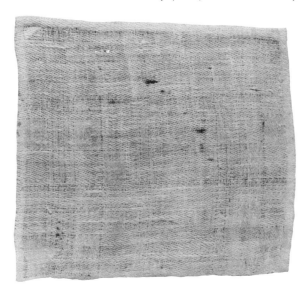

Fig. 7
Tablecloth. Warp: undyed single Z-twist linen, 58 per inch; weft: undyed single Z-twist linen, 54 per inch; edges: 2 selvage, 2 hemmed, all with cotton knotted fringe added (3 1/2″); size: 70 1/4 x 33 3/4 + 33 3/4″ (seamed in center); repeat: 3 x 3″ Londonderry (N.H.) Historical Society.

A poem which John Campbell, the Windham farmer, copied into his diary from a Portsmouth newspaper suggests the high-spirited nature of these events:

> Three or four peadlars three or four packs
> Three or four hucksters emptying sacks
> Three or four hustlers selling their gin
> Three or four sharpers taking folks in
> Three or four boys with three or four misses
> From them expecting three or four kisses
> Three or four Beakers atraficking Bread
> Three or four Fiddlers pretty near Dead . . .
> Three or four fools stript to the buff
> Three of four Noses Bloody enoof
> Three or four Bullyes Bound over to Cort
> And three or four Vendues Ends all the sport.[21]

Early in the eighteenth century, the Londonderry fair represented a unique Scotch-Irish culture, but later "the Irish and Yankee customs were gently intermingled."[22] "The Scotch jig, the Highland fling, Irish reel and Yankee breakdown were blended together in innocent merrymaking."[23] Just as the English and Scotch-Irish traditions increasingly influenced one another in the Londonderry fair, so the tradition of linen-making within each ethnic group gradually combined to form a new, American culture. English settlers married Ulster Scots, and passed along to their children the ancient methods for flax-dressing, spinning and weaving. Stimulated by government bounties, trained in spinning schools, and responsive to new markets both within New England and to the south and west, a new generation of Americans established a linen industry with a distinctive Yankee stamp. Through the 1750s, the textile trade with Europe remained vigorous, but New Englanders had set a firm foundation for domestic industrial independence.

With the crises which culminated in the American Revolution, the ability of the colonists to produce enough linen for their own needs was put to the test. The Sugar Act, passed by Parliament in 1764, was the first of several acts which taxed imported textiles, sharply restricting available supplies and cutting into the business of colonial merchants. Between 1765 and 1767, the Stamp Act and Townshend Duties united merchants, urban laborers, and back-country farmers

20

in rebellion. Enraged citizens declared a boycott against imported goods, calling for the rapid development of American textile production. One rhymester penned these lines in the *Boston Post-Boy and Advertiser:*

> First then throw aside your high top knots of pride
> Wear none but your own country linen
> Of economy boast. Let your pride be the most
> To show cloaths of your own make and spinning.

The city of Providence, Rhode Island offered a prize for the largest amount of flax to be raised in 1766. Forming clubs with names like the Daughters of Liberty and the Association of Plantation Maidens, women held spinning bees such as the one described in a Providence newspaper:

> On the 4th instant, *eighteen daughters of liberty*, young ladies of good reputation, assembled at the house of doctor *Ephraim Bowen*, in this town, in consequence of an invitation of that gentleman, who had discovered a laudable zeal for the introducing *Home Manufactures*. There they exhibited a fine example of industry, by spinning from sunrise until dark, and displayed a spirit for saving their sinking country, rarely to be found among persons of more age and experience.

In Salisbury, Byfield, Newbury, and Boston, Massachusetts, groups of up to forty-five women gathered on their ministers' lawns to spin cotton and linen yarns, sunrise to sunset.[24]

One should not assume too quickly that the rash of spinning bees and rhetoric which followed the Sugar and Stamp Acts had a strong, permanent impact on trade patterns. Once the Revolution was over, merchants resumed importing a wide variety of linen fabrics for sale in New England. A typical advertisement in the *New Hampshire Gazette* in 1797 described, "*Dry Goods,* Received by the arrivals from Europe, a large and general assortment" which included Irish linens and sheetings among many other fabrics. The merchant George Holmes Hall of Brattleboro, Vermont, left an inventory of Indian calico, India cotton and Marseilles quilting as well as pink cambrics, purple cambric, and "bro Holland," when he died in 1807. Although the United States Commissary General's Office purchased

110,380 yards of domestic brown linen and 46,649 yards of tow for the use of the army in 1813, it also bought 7,295 yards of brown linen, 108,799 ells of osnaburg, and 11, 895 yards of ticklenburg, all imported. In 1819, William Dickinson noted in his *General Commercial Dictionary* that "The cambrics now used in this country are chiefly manufactured in Scotland and Ireland, and to such perfection is the manufacture arrived, that now large quantities of them are exported to America." Levi Jackson of Chesterfield, New Hampshire, carried yellow buckram, black cambric, Russia duck, Bro holland, lawn and Irish linen in 1821, distinguished in his inventory from "homemade linen."[25]

If New England spinners and weavers were far from self-sufficient by the turn of the nineteenth century, nevertheless it is clear that "homemade linen" had cut into European trade to a significant degree. Phineas Bond, a British consul living in Philadelphia in 1789, noted, "Among the country people coarse linens in Mass. Bay of their own making are in such general use as to lessen the importation of checks and even coarse Irish linens nearly 2/3ds." Enclaves of flax production could be discovered from Connecticut to Maine. Henry Wansey, traveling near New Haven in 1794, observed that the inhabitants "raise a great deal of flax, and spin it into sheeting, curtains, bed furniture, Ec., of which I saw a great deal manufacturing." Bronson Alcott recalled of northwest Connecticut around 1810, "Flax was cultivated by the farmers as generally as were oats and rye . . . The linen manufacture was an important thing in every household." Scotch linen-makers in Ryegate, Vermont, acquired a local reputation, as did Germans in Broad Bay, Maine.[26]

Because of the state's heritage of Scotch-Irish quality and business acumen, a thriving trade in New Hampshire linen developed. In particular, New Hampshire linen found a market in the South. Jeremy Belknap noted in 1792 that "In most of our country towns considerable quantities of tow-cloth are made, some of which is exported to the Southern States, to Clothe the Negroes, who labor on the plantations." In 1810, Albert Gallatin found that in New Hampshire, "considerable quantities of coarse flaxen cloth, worth from 15¢ to 20¢ per yard, thus manufactured in towns, and sent for a market to the Southern States, on which a profit is made by the trader."[27]

22

In addition to linen cloth, New England farmers sold both raw flax and the by-products of flax processing, including flax seed and linseed oil. Ireland in particular bought American flax seed to supply its own linen manufacture. To satisfy the high demand for New England seed, merchants advertised in the newspapers of small towns. In 1795 John Holbrook of Brattleboro, Vermont, advertised in the *Keene* [New Hampshire] *Rising Sun*, stating that he "wishes to purchase 2000 bushels of Flax seed . . . and will give almost any price for them . . . to sell down the river." Milford, Connecticut alone sold over 4000 bushels of flax seed in 1807. Because linen manufacture remained difficult and costly, many farmers found it more profitable to exchange either the seed or the fiber at the local general store for goods or cash. Around 1820, many customers paid Caleb Stark of Dunbarton, New Hampshire, flax by the pound or flax seed by the bushel in exchange for food, hardware or imported cloth. In Saxton's River, Vermont in the 1830s, Perry and Company were willing to pay 7¢ a pound for white rags, 75¢ a pound for goose feathers, and 6 to 10¢ a pound for flax.[28]

Another saleable product of the flax plant was linseed oil, an essential ingredient in paint and varnishes used for the building trades, cabinet-making, and the arts. Linseed oil itself produced a by-product: the dry oil cake left after the seeds were pressed provided feed for cattle. To meet demand, oil mills were established all over New England to press the seed acquired from local farmers. The first mill appeared in New Haven in 1718, another in Hatfield, Mass., in 1735, and by 1810, one hundred and ten linseed oil mills were scattered across the region.[29]

During the first decade of the nineteenth century, hand linen-making reached its peak in New England. Between 1810 and 1820, factory-made cotton began to emerge as a serious rival to flax as the fiber for everyday textile manufacture. American handweavers first started to use a factory cotton warp with a homespun linen weft in their towels and tablecloths, reversing the pattern common in the days when handspun cotton was too fragile for use as a warp. Gradually cotton cloth made in American factories replaced earlier imported and homespun textiles, as the records of the Burleigh and Frost General Store in Durham, New Hampshire, show. In the accounts of 1797 to

1806, customers bought mostly India cotton, shalloon and "casemere," as well as substantial quantities of cotton wool, or cotton by the pound ready for spinning. They often paid for these purchases with homemade tow cloth. After 1818, the accounts begin to include such purchases as "6 3/4 yds Fac'y 38c thread," "7 yds Fac. Shirg [shirting]" and "10 yds. Fac. Sheetg." Phillips Bartlett bought six yards of factory gingham at the store in 1821, and Jacob Odell, two yards of mixed satinett, a lightweight cotton and wool combination produced in the first mills of New England. The shift came a little earlier in the Putnam and Perkins General Stores of Fitchburg and Lunenburg, Massachusetts, where "factory gingham" began to appear in 1813. The products of New England mills were sold alongside "homemade cloth and thread" in that year, and "English goods," "Rushia sheeting" and such imported cloths continued to compete with the new fabrics into the 1820s. In Belfast, Maine, "factory warp," "factory cloth," and "factory shirting" were all available by 1817 at William Ryan's store.[30]

Cotton's advantage over linen lay first in the fiber itself, which was easily accessible from the plant and tough enough to take some abuse in handling. By 1804, New England entrepreneurs could invest in either of two cotton spinning machines, each with significant advantages, long before any flax spinning machinery had been perfected. The water-powered spinning frame, invented by Arkwright in the 1770s and introduced into the United States by Samuel Slater in 1790, could be operated by unskilled women and children at low wages, though it produced relatively coarse yarn. The spinning mule, introduced after 1804, required skilled and hence male labor, but spun fine grades of cotton yarn at a rate forty-five times that of the hand spinning wheel. With the invention of the cotton gin in 1793, abundant supplies of this fiber became available from the southern states, and cotton mills sprang up all over New England. Between 1805 and 1832, at least 450 cotton mills operated for some period of time in New England (fig. 8). Towns where both Scotch-Irish and Yankees had developed linen-making into an art in the eighteenth century boasted of cotton mills in the nineteenth. New England youths, male and female, gave up tedious hand cloth-making to work in the factories, where, as one observer noted in 1832, "a female can now earn more cloth in a day than she could make in the household way in a week."[31]

Fig. 8
Lower Bridge and Factories, Dover, N.H. Thomas Edwards (Boston: 1831)
Lithograph. Boston Athenaeum.

Linen manufacture, in contrast to cotton, remained in the handicraft stage: labor intensive and costly. The horticultural skills needed to raise flax were always in short supply in New England; the labor required to plant, pull and dress flax made that fiber a more expensive raw material than cotton raised and ginned by slaves. With its combination of delicate fiber and tough bark and core, the flax stalk resisted machine handling. Attempts to mechanize hackling only resulted in turning the valuable long fibers into useless tow, leaving the skilled flax-dresser secure in his prestigious craft. Around 1806 the gill frame, which could spin flax, was introduced in Europe. Before 1823 a sail-cloth manufactory in Paterson, New Jersey, and several small mills in New York and Pennsylvania had introduced these spinning machines. These mills could only spin the coarsest yarns, however. Not until 1825 was a wet-spinning process capable of spinning fine thread perfected. It, too, required skilled workers. Among all the steps in processing flax, only braking and scutching (swingling) had been successfully adapted to water power by 1820. So-called scutching mills, which employed machines with fluted wooden rollers to break and rotating blades to swingle the flax, were common in Ireland at this time. One appeared in New York in 1823, and New Englanders may have erected some as well. But beset by a chronic labor shortage and offered the cheap alternative of the cotton mill, few American entrepreneurs would invest in a mechanical process for which most of the steps had to be carried out by highly paid, skilled workers.[32]

The limited extent of industrial linen-making in New England in the nineteenth century reflected the advantages of cotton manufacture. Three companies successfully manufactured linen in Massachusetts: Smith and Dove in Andover starting in 1835, Stevens in Dudley after 1846, and American Linen in Fall River beginning in 1852. Shorter-lived mills also produced some linen in Braintree, Walpole, and Ludlow, Massachusetts. At a New York exhibition in 1855, American Linen displayed several fabrics woven on power looms, including diaper, sheeting, towelling, coatings, crash, tablecloths, napkins, and pillowcases. The bulk of flax products made in these factories, however, represented the more pedestrian sail twines, shoe threads, and crash towelling requiring fewer skilled hacklers and wet-spinners, and the total labor force of the mills was no more than 1500 employees in 1875.[33]

It would be difficult to overestimate the devastating impact of mechanization on the household linen industry in New England. As Clarence Day noted, "Flax was the first crop to be abandoned. Farmers and their wives gladly gave up the drudgery of preparing flax and weaving linen as soon as factory-woven cloth made from cotton was priced within their reach." In 1835 Henry Colman wrote in the *New England Farmer*, "Of flax very little is cultivated, excepting that here and there a farmer raises a small quantity for thread in his family. The extensive and daily extending use of cotton, seems likely to almost entirely supersede, the use of flax." Flax seed for export to Ireland became a much more profitable commodity than linen cloth, so farmers "suffered [the seed] to grow ripe that [it] may pay the expense of the culture." As a result, by the 1830s, "a domestic manufactured linen shirt [was] as rare as a white colt."[34]

The demise of household linen manufacturing in New England signalled the beginning of the end of the agricultural way of life in the region, and the birth of a new social system. When families bought cloth in town, young women who had been groomed to work at home found themselves less crucial to the functioning of the domestic economy and free to go to work in a cotton mill or to take up schoolteaching. Young men gradually gave up the hardscrabble existence of farm labor and sought the wages of factory jobs. Once central to community life as well as to cloth production, the neighborly networks needed to cultivate and process flax in season broke down. New England left behind the tedium of producing linen by hand labor, but it gave up the familiar rhythms of seasonal work and the close ties which bound the agricultural community together. The opening of the industrial era brought new kinds of work ordered by the relentless mill bell and new, impersonal relations between boss and worker.

At mid-century, the art of hand linen-making had almost entirely disappeared. In 1863, Sylvester Judd, historian of Hadley, Massachusetts, adopted a tone of nostalgia when he wrote of flax processing:

> So complete had been the change that few persons under 30 years of age, have ever seen a woman hatchel flax or card tow, or heard the buzzing of the foot wheel ... The flax dresser, with the shives, fibres and dirt of flax covering his garments, and his face begrimed with dust, has

disappeared; the noise of his brake and swingling knife has ended, and the boys no longer make bonfires of his swingling tow. The sound of the spinning wheel, the song of the spinster and the snapping of the clock-reel have all ceased . . . The spinning woman of King Lemuel cannot be found.[35]

Handmade linens of the eighteenth century were already becoming antiquarian curiosities. At the Hillsborough (New Hampshire) County Fair of 1854, Miss Lucy Damon of Milford was awarded a prize for "a linen table cover, made in her father's family more than forty years since, and *patched by herself in more than 100 places.*" Such artifacts competed at the agricultural fairs with a few newly-made linen tablecloths or towels, such as the "18 pieces of home wrought old fashioned damask" which won a prize at the New Hampshire State Fair of 1853. In addition, farm families in the most remote rural parts of New England continued to manufacture small quantities of linen for local use sometimes, but not always, in com-bination with a warp thread of machine-spun cotton. Olive Sargent of Brattleboro, Vermont, for instance, earned a living by weaving home-made linens into the 1840s.[36]

By 1860, though, even such remainders of the once-thriving linen industry had died out. The *Census of Manufacturing* for 1860 included the first historical survey of American linen, describing its production in the preindustrial period and its failure to adapt suc-cessfully to mechanization. In general, the *Census* found that "with the increase of the cotton culture and manufacture, and the improve-ments in cotton and woolen machinery, cotton has been extensively substituted for flax and hemp even in household manufactures, which have generally been abandoned for the products of regular factories, either domestic or foreign."[37] For most New Englanders, King Cotton reigned. The making of homespun linen, and the way of life surrounding it, had passed into history.

NOTES

1. David A. Pennington and Michael B. Taylor, *A Pictorial Guide to American Spinning Wheels* (Sabbathday Lake, Maine: 1975), pp. 19-24; *CIBA Review* 28 (December 1939), pp. 996-997; Dorothy K. MacDonald, *Fibres, Spindles and Spinning-Wheels* (Toronto: 1950), pp. 36-37; John Horner, *The Linen Trade of Europe During the Spinning Wheel Period* (Belfast, Ireland: 1920), pp. 67-68.

2. Horner, *passim*; Alfred S. Moore, *Linen*, Staple Trades and Industries (New York: 1900), p. 45; Betty Messenger, *Picking Up the Linen Threads* (Austin, Texas: 1978), p. 14.

3. William B. Weeden, *Economic and Social History of New England*, Vol. 1 (Boston: 1890), pp. 170, 197; Nathaniel B. Shurtleff, ed., *Records of the Governor and Company of the Massachusetts Bay in New England*, Vol. 1 (Boston: 1853), pp. 294, 303, 320, 376; *The Charter Granted by Their Majesties King William and Queen Mary to the Inhabitants of the Province of the Massachusetts-Bay in New-England* (Boston: 1726), pp. 297-98; U.S. Department of Commerce, Bureau of the Census, *Eighth Census: 1860*, Vol. 3, *Manufactures*, p. cv.; William R. Bagnall, *The Textile Industries of the United States*, Vol. 1 (Cambridge, Mass: 1893), pp. 6-8.

4. "Mr. Pemberton," quoted in Samuel G. Drake, *The History and Antiquities of Boston* (Boston: 1856), pp. 560-61; Rolla Milton Tryon, *Household Manufactures in the United States, 1640-1860* (1917; reprint ed., New York: [1966], pp. 86-88; Bagnall, pp. 18, 36-49; Gary B. Nash, "The Failure of Female Factory Labor in Colonial Boston," *Labor History* 20 (Spring 1979), 165-88; George Francis Dow, *The Arts and Crafts in New England* (Topsfield, Mass: 1927), p. 269; J. Leander Bishop, *A History of American Manufactures 1608-1860*, Vol. 1 (Philadelphia: 1864), pp. 333-35; Weeden, p. 679.

5. "New England's First Fruits" (London: 1643), quoted in Bagnall, p. 6; Abbott Lowell Cummings, ed., *Rural Household Inventories, 1675-1775* (Boston: 1964), pp. 9-13, etc.; Tryon, pp. 81-84.

6. "New England's First Fruits," Bagnall, Vol. 1, p. 6.

7. Cummings, pp. 51-52; Sylvester Judd, *History of Hadley, Massachusetts* (Springfield, Mass.: 1905), p. 387.

8. *Boston Gazette*, June 23/30, 1735, quoted in Dow, p. 155; Account book of John Gilman, New Hampshire Historical Society, Archives; *New Hampshire Gazette*, November 25, 1757, p. 2.

9. Conrad Gill, *The Rise of the Irish Linen Industry* (Oxford: 1925), pp. 30-60; Horner, pp. 17-19; Gordon Woodbury, "The Scotch-Irish and Irish Presbyterian Settlers of New Hampshire," *Proceedings of the New Hampshire Historical Society* 4 (1899-1905), p. 147; R.J. Dickson, *Ulster Emigration to Colonial America, 1718-1775* (London: 1966), pp. 7-9; James G. Leyburn, *The Scotch-Irish: a Social History* (Chapel Hill, N.C.: 1962), p. 159.

10. Horner, p. 22; Leyburn, p. 101; John M. Whiton, *Sketches of the History of New Hampshire* (Concord, N.H.: 1834), p. 66; Albert Smith, *History of the Town of Peterborough, New Hampshire* (Boston: 1876), pp. 32-33.

11. Woodbury, pp. 144-51; Leyburn, pp. 159-64, 238-41; Dickson, pp. 7-11; Smith, pp. 33-35; Leonard A. Morrison, *The History of Windham in New Hampshire* (Boston: 1883), pp. 23-24; Jeremy Belknap, *The History of New-Hampshire*, Vol. 2 (Boston: 1791), pp. 35-37; Rev. Edward L. Parker, *The History of Londonderry* (Boston: 1851), pp. 35-60; Personal communication with R. Stuart Wallace.

12. Belknap, Vol. 2, p. 37.

13. Parker, p. 48.

14. Drake, p. 560; Woodbury, p. 155; Morrison, p. 292.

15. George Waldo Browne, ed., *Early Records of Londonderry, Windham, and Derry, New Hampshire 1719-1762* (Manchester, N.H.: 1908), pp. 74, 215, 230, 254-55, 285-87, 290-91, 297, 299; quoted in Robert C. Mack, compiler, *Exercises on the 150th Anniversary of the Settlement of Old Nutfield* (Manchester, N.H.: 1870), p. 62.

16. James Birkit, *Some Cursory Remarks Made . . . in His Voyage to North America, 1750-51*, Yale Historical Manuscripts (New Haven: 1916), p. 11; George Grieve, note to his 1787 translation of Marquis de Chastellux, *Travels in North America* (Chapel Hill, N.C.: 1963), Vol. 1, p. 341.

17. *Diary of Matthew Patten of Bedford, New Hampshire, 1754-88* (Concord, N.H.: 1903), pp. 165, 173; Diary of John Campbell, New Hampshire Historical Society, Archives.

18. Probate inventories of Rockingham County, New Hampshire, in New Hampshire Historical Society, Library; *Diary of Matthew Patten*, pp. 150-51.

19. *Diary of Matthew Patten*, pp. 146, 166, 170.

20. Inventories of Rockingham County, N.H.H.S.; Parker, pp. 51, 100.

21. Parker, pp. 62-63, 93; Letterbook of Gov. John Wentworth, Transcript, New Hampshire Historical Society; *New England Farmer*, October 25, 1817, p. 124; Morrison, p. 293; Diary of John Campbell.

22. *New England Farmer*, October 25, 1817, p. 124.

23. Morrison, p. 293.

24. "Address to the Ladies," *Boston Post-Boy and Advertiser*, November 16, 1767, p. 3; *Boston Chronicle*, April 7, 1766, quoted in Tryon, p. 106; Tryon, p. 107.

25. *New Hampshire Gazette*, August 1, 1797, p. 2; Probate inventories compiled by Caroline Sloat, Old Sturbridge Village; "Articles, Foreign and Domestic, Consumed in Clothing the Army and Navy of the United States in the Year 1813, and an Estimate for 1814," report #410 in *American State Papers: Documents, Legislative and Executive, of the Congress of the United States* 6, *Finances*, 1832, pp. 817-18; William Dickinson, ed., *A General Commercial Dictionary*, 2d edition (London: 1819), p. 185.

26. Tryon, p. 132; David John Jeremy, *Henry Wansey and His American Journal* (Philadelphia: 1970), p. 71; Howard S. Russell, *A Long Deep Furrow: Three Centuries of Farming in New England* (Hanover, N.H.: 1976), pp. 141, 297-98.

27. Belknap, Vol. 2, p. 161; Albert Gallatin, "Manufactures," report #325 in *American State Papers* 6, *Finances*, 1832, p. 435.

28. *Keene* (N.H.) *Rising Sun*, August 11, 1795; *New Hampshire Sentinel*, August 22, 1801; Russell, pp. 117, 297; Account book of Caleb Stark, Dunbarton, New Hampshire, New Hampshire Historical Society, Archives; Notes supplied by Caroline Sloat, Old Sturbridge Village.

29. Judd, p. 377; Tench Coxe, *A Statement of the Arts and Manufactures of the United States for the Year 1810* (1813; reprinted, in *American Industry and Manufactures in the Nineteenth Century: A Basic Source Collection*, Vol. 2, Elmsford, N.Y.: 1970), p. 21.

30. Day book of Burleigh and Frost, Durham, New Hampshire, Harvard University Baker Library; Day book of Putnam and Perkins, Fitchburg and Lunenburg, Massachusetts, Harvard University Baker Library; Day book of William Ryan, Belfast, Maine, Old Sturbridge Village, Archives.

31. Caroline F. Ware, *The Early New England Cotton Manufacture: a Study in Industrial Beginnings* (Boston: 1931), pp. 22-35; Victor S. Clark, *History of Manufactures in the Unites States*, Vol. 1 (1929; reprint ed., 1949),

pp. 422-30; Aaron Tufts of Dudley, Massachusetts, 1832, quoted in Louis McLane, *Documents Relative to the Manufactures in the United States*, Vol. 1, (1833; reprint ed., 1969), pp. 68-69.

32. Clark, pp. 423-24; Gill, pp. 316-17; S.W. Pomeroy, "Essays on Flax Husbandry," *New England Farmer*, September 6, 1823, pp. 14-15; March 9, 1831, p. 269; Ulster Museum, "Water Power and its Application to Flax Scutching in Ulster," n.d.; Abraham Rees, "Flax," *Cyclopaedia* 15 (Philadelphia: 1822).

33. Orra L. Stone, *History of Massachusetts Industries* (Boston: 1930), pp. 406-09; Clark, 1, p. 532; *Eighth Census*: 1860, *Manufactures*, p. cx; Massachusetts Bureau of Statistics of Labor, *Census of Massachusetts*, 1875, Vol. 2, *Manufactures and Occupations*, p. 486; McLane, Vol. 1, pp. 396-97.

34. Clarence Day, *A History of Maine Agriculture 1604-1860* (Orono, Maine: 1954), p. 155; Henry Colman, "Notes by the Way," *New England Farmer*, November 18, 1835, p. 148; Rodolphus Dickinson, *A Geographical and Statistical View of Massachusetts Proper* (Greenfield, Mass.: 1815), p. 9; "Flax," *New England Farmer*, February 9, 1831, p. 233.

35. Judd, p. 359.

36. *Transactions of the New Hampshire State Agricultural Society*, 1853 (Concord: 1854), p. 117; *Transactions*, 1854 (Concord: 1855), p. 311; Account book of Olive Sargent, Old Sturbridge Village.

37. *Eighth Census*: 1860, *Manufactures*, p. civ.

[Braking & scutching] "January," *Maine Farmer's Almanac* (Hallowell: 1831)
Wood engraving.

PREINDUSTRIAL LINEN-MAKING:

THE PROCESS

FLAX INTO LINEN

Making linen from flax is a labor-intensive process requiring patience and skill.

The flax stalk is a woody cylinder surrounded by strong silky fibers and encased in a tough outer bark, all cemented together by a glue-like substance. In order to free the fibers for spinning, the glue must be dissolved and the woody core and bark broken up and removed. Once the delicate fibers are cleaned and softened they can be spun and woven.

Linen cloth is strong and resistant to abrasion, even when wet. Unlike woolen cloth, it will neither lose its shape nor wear out when washed vigorously. Linen absorbs water naturally, making it useful for towels as well as comfortable in sticky weather. Linen takes dye poorly in comparison to other fibers, but its natural brown color can be bleached to a gleaming white. As a piece of linen is used over the years, the wax and gummy materials which bind flax fibers together become glazed and small amounts of remaining woody matter are removed, so that the fabric develops a lovely luster.

[Diagram and cross section of flax fiber] J. Merritt Matthews, *The Textile Fibres*, p. 277 (N.Y.: 1908) Photo-engraving.

Diagram of flax straw:

1. marrow
2. woody fiber
3. cambium layer
4. bast fiber
5. rind or bark

1. 2. 3. 4. 5.

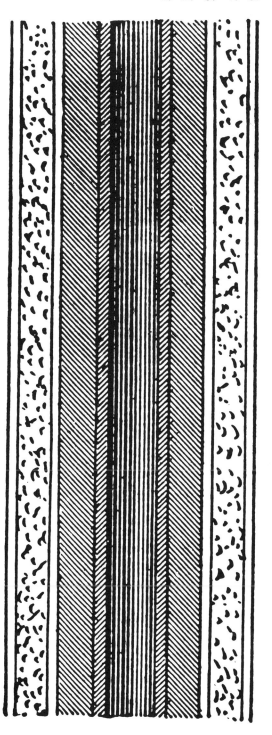

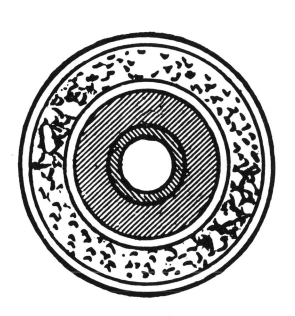

SOWING

The early New England farmer began the cycle of flax culture in late March or early April, when flax seeds were sown in moist, rich soil. The thicker the seeds were sown, the finer the stalk of the plant which grew up, and the better the quality of the resulting linen thread. One colonial author observed, "Flax should be sowed promiscuously (as Wheat or Oats, &c.) but somewhat thicker . . . It will take a Bushel and a Half to sow one Acre of Land to make it fit for Linen or Thread."[1]

1. John Wily, *A Treatise on the Propagation of Sheep, the Manufacture of Wool, and the Cultivation and Manufacture of Flax.* (Williamsburg: F. Royle, 1765) pp. 31-32.

" . . . Sowing the Flax Seed . . . " Hincks, Plate I, detail.

PULLING

As soon as the leaves on the flax plant turned yellow and the lower
leaves fell off, most of the seeds were ripe and the crop was ready
to harvest. Usually the flax was ready to be pulled in July. A strong
farm worker had to grasp bunches of the flax in the center of the stalk
and pull them out by the roots, gathering in one direction, to prevent
tangling among the plants. The plants were then allowed to dry.

"Linum sativum. Garden Flax." *The Herbal or General Historie of Plants* by John
Gerard, enlarged and amended by Thomas Johnson. Chap. 166, Book 2, p. 566
(London: 1633; reprint edition, N.Y.: 1975) Wood engraving.

[Pulling the flax plant] "Strappare il lino," [G.B. Trecco], *Coltivazione e
Governo del Lino Marzuolo*, Plate 2 (Vicenza, Italy: 1792) Engraving.   38

RIPPLING

The best method for removing seeds from the flax was to pull the fibers through a rippling comb until all the seeds fell off. Two other methods — whipping the flax on a small cask, and threshing it with a flail — were also used in New England, but these caused the fibers to tangle and some of the fine, long fibers to shatter.

RIPPLING COMB New England. Ipswich (Mass.) Historical Society.
19 1/4 x 6 1/2 x 8″

" . . . Rip[p]ling or saving the Seed . . . " Hincks, Plate II, detail.   **40**

RETTING

By retting – soaking the flax in a stream or a dewy field – the gummy sap which bound the valuable fiber to the bark was rotted away. For water retting, the sheaves of flax were anchored down in a pond, lake or stream. If the flax was to be dew-retted, it was laid out in a field and exposed to rain and dew. Besides causing a disagreeable odor, retting demanded careful judgment on the part of the farmer to prevent under- or over-watering. John Wily remarked, "The watering or rotting Flax is looked upon to be the most mysterious and difficult part of the whole Manufacture . . . it is out of the Power of any Man to tell the exact Number of Days it will take to water or dew-rot Flax."[2] He preferred a stream for retting because "the running Water being cooler than Pond Water it will not rot too soon,"[3] but New England farmers usually practiced dew retting because of the abundant dews characteristic of the region.

2. *Ibid.* p. 35.
3. *Ibid.* p. 36.

[Retting] " . . . *Boging or Burying it in Water* . . . " Hincks, Plate II, detail.

BRAKING

The retted flax plant contained a pulpy core which was separated from the surrounding fibers by being broken into pieces. The most common method employed a flax brake. Draping the flax over the horizontal base of the brake, the worker struck it sharply from above with a second set of boards, shifting the flax gradually until all the core and bark had been broken. Sometimes beatles were used instead of a brake; the worker laid the flax on a hard surface and beat it with the heavy mallet end of the tool until the flax was soft. Wily wrote, "A Brake is the most expeditious Method for breaking Flax, . . . but it is apter to make a larger Quantity of Tow, [short, coarse fibers] . . . that which is done with Beatles . . . will take a longer Time . . ."[4]

4. *Ibid.* p. 41.

FLAX BRAKE New England. MVTM 59.1.47
44 x 17 1/2 x 33 1/4"

Braking, *Maine Farmer's Almanac*

[Beetling] "Pestare il lino," Trecco, Plate 7

SCUTCHING

Scutching, also called swingling, transformed the flax into soft, pliable fiber by removing any hard pieces. The worker hung the flax over the side of a scutching board, where he struck it with a wooden knife in a continuous scraping motion down the side of the flax. This process was repeated until the flax was free of the hard or gummy residue. Under the motion of the scutching knife, the long, fine fibers became separated from the short, coarse tow, which fell to the ground.

Scutching, *Maine Farmer's Almanac*,

" . . . *the common method of . . . Scutching . . .* " Hincks, Plate IV, detail.

HACKLING

Hackling (also called heckling or hetcheling) involved drawing bunches of flax fibers through a series of one to three combs graduated from coarse to fine. Any remaining hard pieces or gum were thus separated from the fibers and the longer fibers were completely separated from the tow. Tow could be collected from the hackle and used to make coarse linen for everyday shirts and bags. If too much tow was left clinging to the long fibers, however, a poor quality of linen would result. A skillful hackler, who handled his flax so that all of the waste was removed but none of the best fibers were shredded into tow, was much in demand and might earn his living travelling from town to town.

" . . . *the common method of . . . Hackling the Flax.*" Hincks, Plate IV, detail.   48

HACKLE (Coarse) Made in 1739. Manchester Historic Association 6860
15 1/2 x 8 1/2 x 7"

HACKLE (Medium) Made in 1777. MVTM 59.1.119
13 1/4 x 3 x 3 3/4"

HACKLE (Fine) New England (?) MVTM 68.56.7
16 1/2 x 5 x 4"

HACKLE (Medium) with cover. MVTM 59.1.110
22 3/4 x 18 x 22"

SPINNING

On a Saxony or low Irish wheel, the long, fine flax fibers were spun into yarn for clothing, towels and tablecloths. The processed flax was dressed onto a distaff in a fine web, allowing the spinner to draw strands of the fibers into a uniform, continuous yarn. The Saxony wheel has one double drive band which controls both the bobbin and flyer, so that the differential motion between them causes the fibers to twist around each other and at the same time be drawn onto the bobbin. To make coarse yarn for ticking and sacking from the tow, the spinner used a cruder wheel.

" . . . *Spinning* . . . " Hincks, Plate VI, detail.

FLAX WHEEL (Low Irish) Made by Hugh Ramsey (1754-1831)
of Holderness, N.H. MVTM 62.2.2

35 1/2 x 22 1/2 x 35"

FLAX WHEEL (Low Irish) Made by D.R. for the Philbrick family of Weare, N.H.
New Hampshire Historical Society 1968.40a-e.
34 x 22 x 34"

FLAX WHEEL (Chair-type, double-pedal) Essex Institute 117,383
20 x 20 x 45"

FLAX WHEEL (Two-spindle, with plying attachment) New Hampshire.
MVTM 59.1.141
20 x 17 1/2 x 36 1/2"

TOW WHEEL New England. MVTM 59.1.139
22 3/4 x 20 x 39 1/4″

HANKING

To remove the yarn from the bobbin and wind it into measured skeins, the spinster used a niddy noddy or a clock reel. The niddy noddy was light and easy to make, but the clock reel was operated more quickly and caused fewer errors. Clock reels employed a series of gears to trigger a noisemaking device when a certain amount of yarn had been wound, usually forty turns to one skein of yarn.

" . . . *Reeling with the Clock Reel* . . . " Hincks, Plate VI, detail.

CLOCK REEL   Made in 1789 by Oliver Dow, probably of Londonderry, N.H.
Currier Gallery of Art
24 x 15 x 41″

CLOCK REEL, detail.

NIDDY-NODDY MVTM 59.1.318
11 3/4 x 7/8 x 18″

WARPING

Weaving involves interlacing lengthwise yarns called the warp with the weft, or crosswise yarns. Warping, or setting up the stationary warp threads on the warp beams of the loom, was complicated because of the danger of tangling or breaking the threads. In order to keep the threads in order and the tension even, a weaver transferred the yarn between a series of tools and finally to the warp beam. First, a skein of yarn was placed on a swift, from which it was wound onto spools using a spool winder. The spools were then arranged on a rack called a creel. Gathering a few threads together at a time, and carefully unwinding them from the spools, the weaver wound the threads onto a warping reel or bars to a predetermined length. The yarns were then transferred under tension to the loom's warp beam. In this process, the weaver achieved the correct width and density for the desired fabric.

Compared to warping, preparing the weft was a simple process. The spool winder doubled as a quill winder. Quills wound with yarn were placed onto the shuttles which would carry the weft back and forth as the weaver created the cloth.

WEAVING

Handlooms used in early New England differed little from those which had become common in Europe during the middle ages. Each loom had at least two harnesses, through which the warp threads were passed. By stepping upon the treadles connected to the harnesses, the weaver lifted them up and down, creating a passage in the warp for the shuttle. The shuttle was thrown from side to side by hand. After each passage of the shuttle, the weft was driven into the cloth by means of a beater.

To create a length of striped ticking, a plaid kerchief, or a colorful patterned coverlet, a weaver wove together dyed and natural or bleached linen yarns. Such materials as indigo, walnut hulls, and tree bark were used to make dyes of various colors. To weave plain weaves and stripes, a weaver needed a simple, two-harness loom, while four to sixteen harnesses were required for more elaborate patterns.

QUILLER-SWIFT COMBINATION MVTM 59.1.174
81 x 24 1/2 x 44"

LOOM, 4-harness. Used in the Francis Grimes house, Deering, N.H. New Hampshire Historical Society 1976.71.15
72 7/8 x 77 1/4 x 79"

BLEACHING

Unless it was to be dyed or used "brown," linen had to be bleached. John Wily described this tedious process, which took about a month to complete:

1. Soak linen 36 to 40 hours in warm water, rinse and dry.
2. Soak in lye and cow dung 48 hours.
3. Stretch cloth over the grass in a bleach-yard.
4. Wash off the cow dung.
5. Beat cloth with "bat staffs" 2 to 3 hours.
6. Place cloth into boiling lye; soak 24 hours.
7. Wash cloth; stretch it over the bleach-green 24 hours.
8. Beat with bat staffs.
9. Repeat the last three steps for 8 to 10 days.
10. Place cloth in buttermilk for 1 or 2 nights.
11. Wash and beat the cloth again, then stretch it over the bleach-green.
12. Sour it again in buttermilk.
13. Repeat the process for another week, until the cloth is white enough.[5]

The bleaching process became much quicker and more efficient after the 1760s when the Irish developed a bleach powder made of chlorine in lime.

5. *Ibid.* pp. 51-52.

Bleaching.

"Bleaching," Isaac Taylor, *Scenes of Wealth, or Views and Illustrations of Trades, Manufactures, Produce and Commerce* . . . (London: 1826) Engraving.

PREINDUSTRIAL LINEN-MAKING

THE PRODUCTS

Overleaf:
"The Tailor." Edward Hazen, *The Panorama of Professions and Trades* (Philadelphia: 1837) Wood engraving.

WEAVING FOR THE FAMILY

To satisfy their needs for everyday clothing, bedding and kitchen linens, many families did their own weaving. The plain weave which became a tow shirt or a lawn nightshift, the striped patterns typical of bed ticking, and the checks and plaids which brightened aprons and kerchiefs could all be woven on a two-harness loom. Decorative weaves such as M's and O's, overshot and huck-a-buck which are characteristic of towels and tablecloths required a four-harness loom. Traditionally, a young woman would weave a full trousseau of table-wear and bedding before her marriage, embellishing her product with her initials, the date, or a number for rotating the linens embroidered in the corner.

"February," *Maine Farmer's Almanac* (Hallowell: 1831) Wood engraving.

TOWEL (detail)

Made at the Philbrick Farm, Weare, New Hampshire, possibly by Clara Philbrick (1803-1886). 'CP 17' cross-stitched in lower left corner; hanging loop at top. Broken point twill weave, goose eye pattern, four-harness.

> *warp:* undyed single Z-twist linen, 40 per inch
> *weft:* undyed single Z-twist linen, 48 per inch
> *edges:* two selvage, one hemmed, one fringed (3 inch)
> *size:* 34 x 25 inches
> *repeat:* 2 3/4 x 3 inches

Society for the Preservation of New England Antiquities
1949.17A

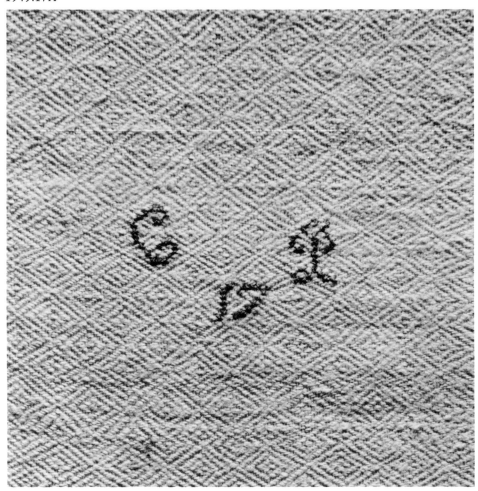

Draft of broken twill weave towel.

All drafts shown illustrate a draw-down for a rising shed loom. The black squares represent weft yarns passing over warp yarns.

Threading

69

TOWEL (detail)

Made by Sarah Putnam Bradford (1746-1822), of Lyndeboro, New Hampshire. Hanging loop at hemmed end. M's and O's weave, three-block, four-harness.

warp:	undyed single Z-twist linen, 38 per inch
weft:	undyed single Z-twist linen, 66 per inch
edges:	two selvage, one hemmed, one fringe (worn)
size:	35 x 19 1/2 inches
repeat:	3/4 x 1 inches

New Hampshire Historical Society
1939.21.2

Draft of M's and O's weave towel.

Threading

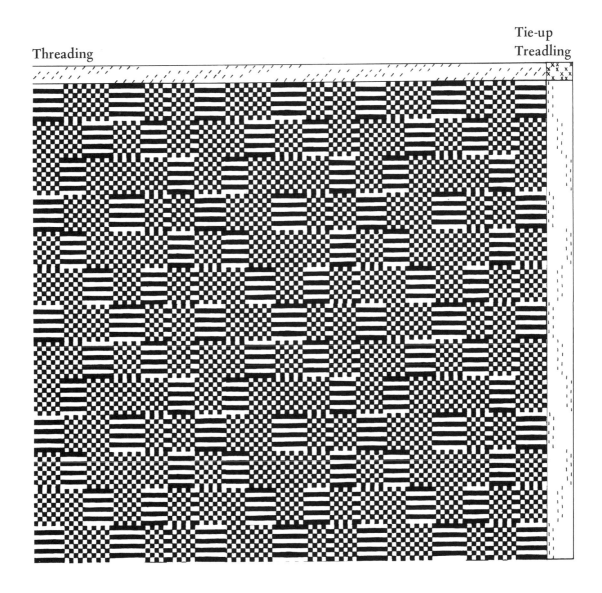

TOWEL (detail)

Made by Anna Scribner Sanborn (*ca*. 1740-1811) of Poplin (now Fremont), New Hampshire. 'AS' cross-stitched at lower center, hanging loop at hemmed end. Overshot weave, four-harness.

warp: undyed single Z-twist linen, 34 per inch
weft: undyed single Z-twist linen, 36 per inch
edges: two selvage, one hemmed, one knotted fringe (4 inches)
size: 31 3/4 x 21 1/4 inches
repeat: 3 1/2 x 3 inches

Currier Gallery of Art
P.C.S. 104 (55)

72

Draft of overshot weave towel.

This draft indicates the pattern picks, each of which is followed by a tabby pick (shown only in the treadling).

Threading

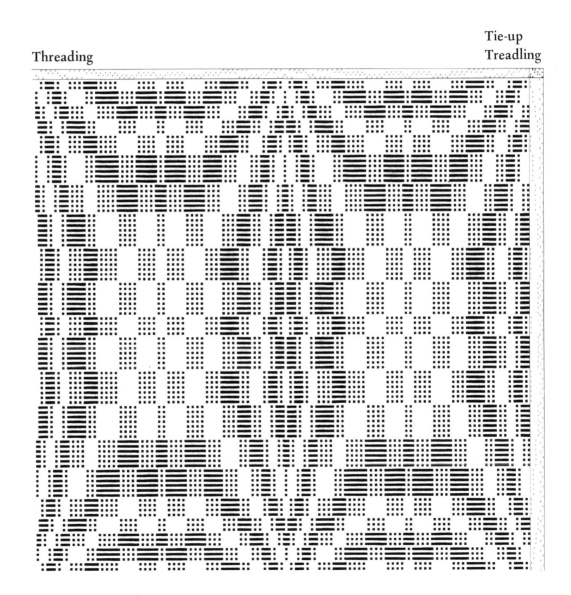

TOWEL (detail)

Made by Elizabeth Needham Jaquith (1748-1820) of Billerica, Massachusetts, for her daughter Abigail (1788-1844). 'AJ' cross-stitched at center of one end. Huck weave, four-harness.

warp:	undyed single Z-twist linen, 44 per inch
weft:	undyed single Z-twist linen, 40 per inch
edges:	two selvage, two hemmed
size:	33 3/4 x 22 1/2 inches
repeat:	1 1/2 x 1 1/2 inches

Society for the Preservation of New England Antiquities
1946.293B

Draft of huck weave towel.

This draft indicates the pattern picks, each of which is followed by a tabby pick (shown only in the treadling).

Threading

TOWEL (detail)

Made at the Philbrick Farm, Weare, New Hampshire, possibly by Clara Philbrick (1803-1886). 'CP23' cross-stitched at lower left of the fringed end. Huck weave, five-harness.

warp:	undyed single Z-twist cotton, 56 per inch
weft:	undyed single Z-twist linen, 42 per inch
edges:	two selvage, one hemmed, one fringed (3 inch)
size:	35 1/2 x 28 inches
repeat:	2 3/4 x 3 inches

Society for the Preservation of New England Antiquities
1949.17A

TOWEL (detail)

Made by Nancy Dexter Whipple (1761-1811) of Cumberland, Rhode Island. 'NDW' cross-stitched in lower center; braided loop at top and bottom. Twill/point twill weave, four-harness.

warp: undyed single Z-twist linen, 44 per inch
weft: undyed single Z-twist linen, 44 per inch
edges: two selvage, two hemmed
size: 31 3/4 x 23 1/2 inches
repeat: 1 1/4 x 1 1/4 inches

Society for the Preservation of New England Antiquities
1959.460.11

TOWEL (detail)

Made by Dorothy Titus of Goffstown, New Hampshire in 1815.
Extended point twill weave, eight-harness.

warp: undyed single Z-twist linen, 56 per inch
weft: undyed single Z-twist linen, 50 per inch
edges: one selvage, three hemmed
size: 16 1/4 x 16 1/2 inches
repeat: 2 1/2 x 2 1/2 inches

Manchester Historic Association
1251

TABLECLOTH (detail)

Made at the James Kennedy Farm, Goffstown, New Hampshire, by Sarah Kennedy Stevens (1794-?). M's and O's weave, four-harness.

> *warp:* undyed single Z-twist linen, 44 per inch
> *weft:* undyed single Z-twist linen, 50 per inch
> *edges:* two selvage, two hemmed
> *size:* 61 1/2 x 28 1/2 inches
> *repeat:* 2 x 2 inches

Manchester Historic Association
5824

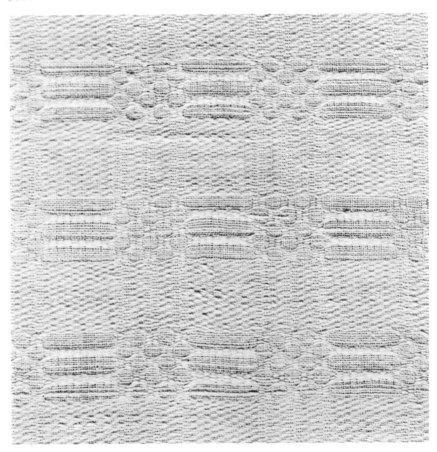

TABLECLOTH (detail)

Made by Anna Scribner Sanborn (*ca.* 1740-1811) of Poplin (now Fremont), New Hampshire. 'AS' cross-stitched at center of one end; seamed in center. Overshot weave, four-harness.

warp: undyed single Z-twist linen, 42 per inch
weft: undyed single Z-twist linen, 50 per inch
edges: two selvage, two hemmed
size: 69 x 33 1/2 + 33 1/2 inches
repeat: 8 x 7 inches

Currier Gallery of Art
P.C.S. 105 (55)

TABLECLOTH (detail)

Made at the Philbrick Farm, Weare, New Hampshire, possibly by Clara Philbrick (1803-1886). 'CP2' once cross-stitched in one corner; seamed in center. Huck weave, five-harness.

> *warp:* undyed single Z-twist linen, 50 per inch
> *weft:* undyed single Z-twist linen, 52 per inch
> *edges:* two selvage, two hemmed
> *size:* 67 x 29 1/2 + 29 1/2 inches
> *repeat:* 4 x 4 inches

Society for the Preservation of New England Antiquities
1949.19B

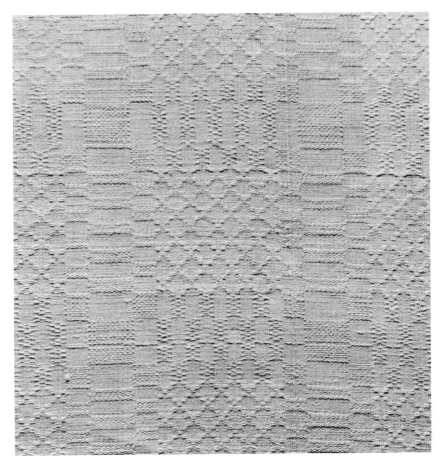

TABLECLOTH (detail)

Made by Sarah Butterfield Tufts (1790-1868) of Kennebec County, Maine. Huck weave, five-harness, seamed in center.

warp:	undyed single Z-twist cotton, 44 per inch
weft:	undyed single Z-twist linen, 56 per inch
edges:	four hemmed with cotton knotted fringe added (2 1/2 inches)
size:	62 x 27 1/2 + 27 1/2 inches
repeat:	2 x 2 1/4 inches

Society for the Preservation of New England Antiquities
1937.202

SHEET   (detail)

Made by Abigail Clark Veasey (1770-1841) of Brentwood, New Hampshire. 'ACV' written in lower left corner. Plain weave.

warp: undyed single Z-twist linen, 40 per inch
weft: undyed single Z-twist linen, 46 per inch
edges: two selvage, two hemmed
size: 88 1/2 x 33 1/4 + 33 1/4 inches

Private collection of Bessie Swain

PILLOWCASE   (detail)

Made by Betsey Hale Colton of Enfield, Connecticut. 'BC' cross-stitched with silk in center. Plain weave.

   warp: undyed single Z-twist linen, 44 per inch
   weft: undyed single Z-twist linen, 46 per inch
   edges: one hemmed
   size: 35 3/4 x 15 3/4 inches

Old Sturbridge Village
26.22.98

PILLOWCASE   (detail)

Made by Alice Stearns (1764-1855) of Bedford, Massachusetts. 'Allice Stearns, Bedford, Mass.' printed in ink on lower left. Plain weave.

warp: undyed single Z-twist linen, 46 per inch
weft: undyed single Z-twist cotton, 52 per inch
edges: one hemmed
size: 30 1/2 x 16 1/2 inches

Society for the Preservation of New England Antiquities
1946.294B

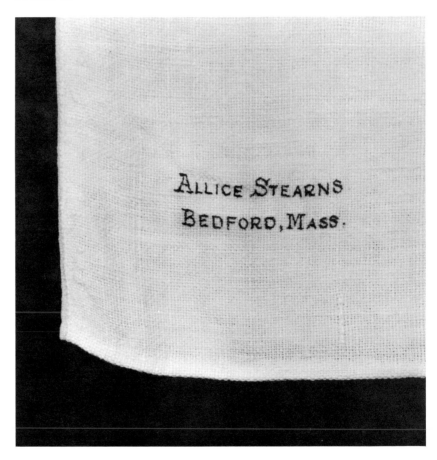

TICKING

Shaped as a mattress with two slits for stuffing with straw. Plain weave.

warp: undyed single Z-twist tow, 34 per inch
weft: undyed single Z-twist tow, 20 per inch
edges: finished
size: 75 1/2 x 55 inches

Society for the Preservation of New England Antiquities
1934.318

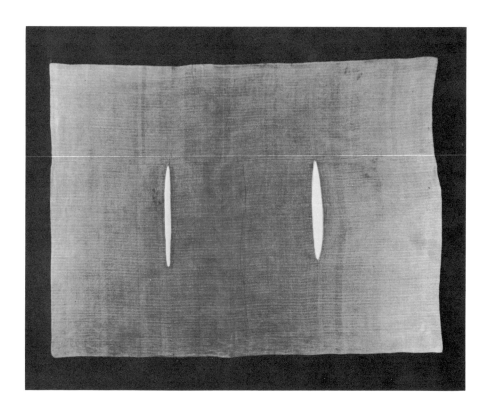

TICKING

Two fragments sewn together.

1. Large piece. Plain weave.

    warp: undyed and blue single
               Z-twist linen,
               42 per inch

    weft: undyed Z-twist linen,
               36 per inch

    size: 77 1/2 x 11 1/2 inches

2. Small piece. Twill weave.

    warp: undyed, blue and brown
               single Z-twist linen,
               52 per inch

    weft: undyed single Z-twist
               linen, 40 per inch

    size: 17 1/2 x 10 1/2 inches

Society for the Preservation of New England Antiquities
1941.769

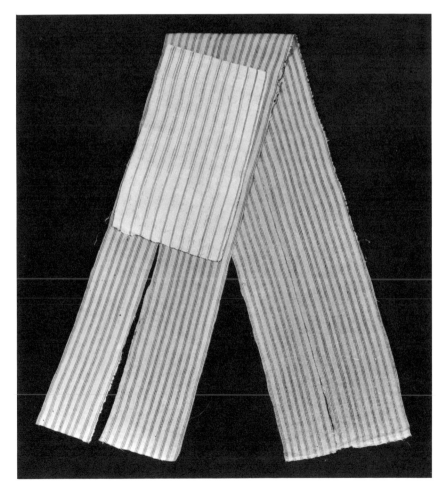

KERCHIEF   (right)

Made at the Elijah Gove Farm, Weare, New Hampshire, possibly by Hannah Gove Philbrick (1774-1838). 'HP' cross-stitched in one corner. Plain weave.

  warp: undyed and gold single Z-twist linen, 38 per inch
  weft: undyed and gold single Z-twist linen, 42 per inch
  edges: two selvage, two hemmed
  size: 23 x 23 inches

Society for the Preservation of New England Antiquities
1949.24E

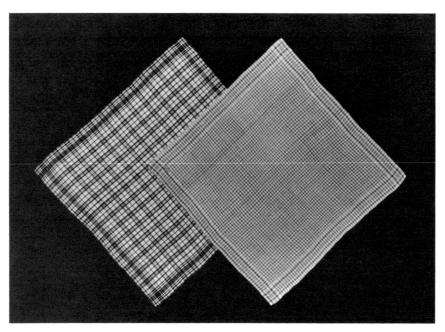

KERCHIEF   (left)

Made at the Elijah Gove Farm, Weare, New Hampshire, possibly by Hannah Gove Philbrick (1774-1838) for her daughter, Clara Philbrick (1803-1886). 'CP' cross-stitched in one corner, 'O' in another corner. Plain weave.

  warp: undyed and blue single Z-twist linen, 40 per inch
  weft: undyed and blue single Z-twist linen, 50 per inch
  edges: two selvage, two hemmed
  size: 24 x 22 1/4 inches

Society for the Preservation of New England Antiquities
1949.24F

KERCHIEF (left)

Made by Mary Patten of Candia, New Hampshire. 'MP' cross-stitched in one corner. Plain weave.

> *warp:* undyed, blue and gold single Z-twist linen, 58 per inch
> *weft:* undyed, blue and gold single Z-twist linen, 50 per inch
> *edges:* two selvage, two hemmed
> *size:* 36 1/4 x 35 1/4 inches

Old Sturbridge Village
26.15.59

KERCHIEFS (center & right)

> *warp:* undyed and blue single Z-twist linen
> *weft:* undyed and blue single Z-twist linen
> *edges:* two selvage, two hemmed

Center kerchief made by Olive Adams Prescott (1780-1860) of Westford, Massachusetts. Plain weave. 34 ¼ x 34 ½ inches
Essex Institute 104,502

Right kerchief made by Betsey Little of Goffstown, New Hampshire. Plain weave. 30 ¼ x 30 ¼ inches

Manchester Historic Association 2258

FIRE BAG

Owned by George Watson (1771-1860) of Salem, Massachusetts. 'N$\underline{o}$1/
Geo$\underline{e}$ Watson/1796.' printed in the center of the bag. Plain weave.

> *warp:* undyed single Z-twist linen, 40 per inch
> *weft:* undyed single Z-twist linen, 32 per inch
> *edges:* one hemmed
> *size:* 52 x 26 1/2 inches

North Andover Historical Society
21.9

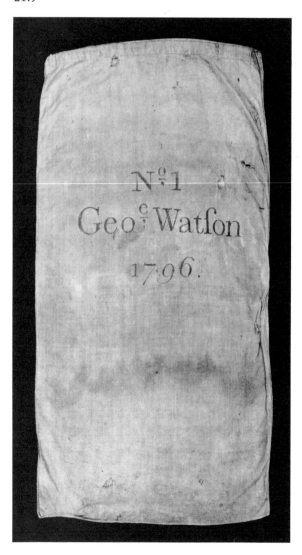

MEAL SACK

Made in Kingston, New Hampshire. Plain weave; illegible printing.

  warp: undyed single Z-twist tow, 20 per inch
  weft: undyed single Z-twist tow, 20 per inch
  edges: overcast seams, one selvage
   size: 38 x 23 1/2 inches

Essex Institute
103,846a

PROFESSIONAL WEAVING

Only a third to half of all New England households owned looms,
so professional weavers were much in demand. Some weavers made
their living largely by weaving lengths of tow, stripes, checks, shirt-
ings, and other simple weaves. Others, highly trained artisans, often
used looms of eight, twelve, or more harnesses to create fancy twill
diaper and damask weaves and coverlets. Although the line between
a talented amateur and a professional weaver is a fine one, linens
made in these complicated patterns are certain to have been woven
by a skilled professional.

"The Manufacturer of Cloth," Edward Hazen, *The Panorama of Professions and
Trades*, p. 42 (Philadelphia: 1837) Wood engraving.

TABLECLOTH (detail)

Made by (or for) Pamela Stone (1801-1850) of Auburn, Massachusetts. 'Pamela Stone/No. 4/1825' signed in ink at both ends, no seam. Satin damask weave, five-block, twenty-five-harness.

warp: undyed single Z-twist linen, 66 per inch
weft: undyed single Z-twist linen, 68 per inch
edges: two selvage, two hemmed
size: 67 1/2 x 66 3/4 inches
repeat: 7 x 17 inches

Old Sturbridge Village
26.13.46

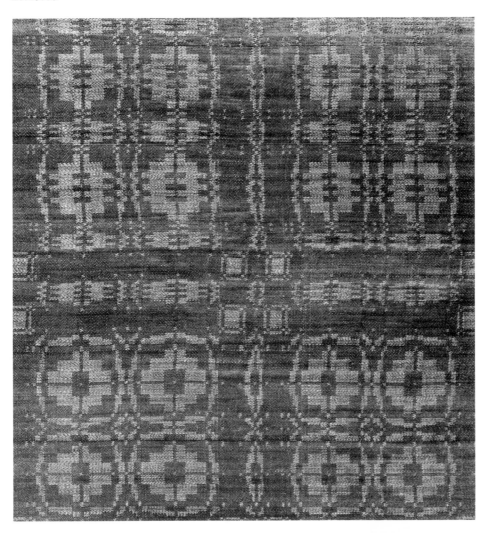

TABLECLOTH   (detail)

Made at the Philbrick Farm, Weare, New Hampshire, possibly by (or for) Clara Philbrick (1803-1886). 'C Philbrick No. 12' cross-stitched at lower center; seamed in the center. Twill diaper (1/3 twill and 3/1 twill) weave, six-blocks.

warp: undyed single Z-twist linen, 58 per inch
weft: undyed single Z-twist linen, 60 per inch
edges: four hemmed
size: 69 x 32 3/4 + 32 3/4 inches
repeat: 2 1/4 x 2 1/4 inches

Society for the Preservation of New England Antiquities
1949.19C

'LINSEY-WOOLSEY' COVERLET

Twill diaper weave, four-block pattern.

warp: undyed two-ply S-twist linen, 30 per inch
weft: green-brown two-ply S-twist wool, 20 per inch
edges: one hemmed, fringe on three sides formed by the warp (6 inches)
and weft (2 1/2 inches)
size: 75 x 34 1/2 + 34 1/2 inches
repeat: 20 x 16 inches

Merrimack Valley Textile Museum
65.52.4

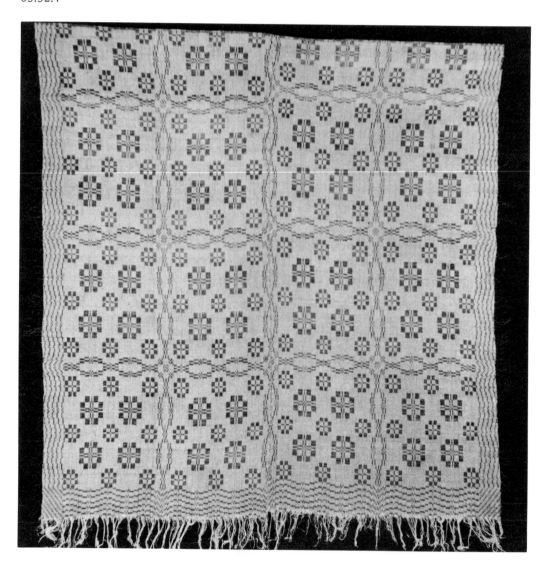

(reverse side)

CLOTHING

Linen was used for summer clothing for men, women and children. Shirts and trousers for men and boys were made of linen or tow, the shortest, coarsest flax fibers. One local historian noted that undergarments of tow were often coarse enough to "render flesh brushes and hair mittens unnecessary."[6] Women sometimes wore linen dresses, although if cotton cloth could be bought, that fabric was often used instead.

Relatively few ordinary linen garments survive today, for after they had worn out, shirts and shifts were recycled as bandages, patches and rags, and as raw materials for papermaking.

6. Georgia Drew Merrill, *History of Carroll County*. (Facsimile of 1889 edition, Somersworth, New Hampshire, 1971) p. 57.

[Spelling book illustration, specimen book of Johnson & Smith, Philadelphia, 1834] reproduced in Clarence P. Hornung, *Handbook of Early American Advertising Art* (New York: Dover Publications, 1947) Wood engraving.

STOCKINGS (right)

'MB' knit into the top of each stocking.

   construction: rib and lace knit
   materials: undyed two-ply Z-twist linen
   size: 26 inches long, 10 inch foot

Old Sturbridge Village
26.17.9a&b

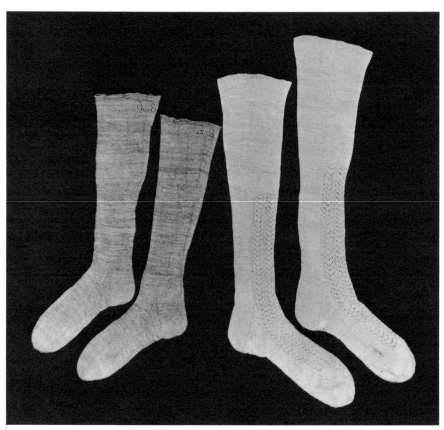

STOCKINGS (left)

Knit by Sarah Prescott Lawrence (1813-?) of Westford, Massachusetts. 'SP' knit into the tops of each stocking.

   construction: rib knit
   materials: undyed single Z-twist linen
   size: 21 inches long, 8 1/2 inch foot

Essex Institute
122,332a&b

TROUSERS

Linen covered buttons. Plain weave.

> *warp:* undyed, brown and blue single Z-twist linen, 58 per inch
> *weft:* undyed single Z-twist linen, 32 per inch
> *edges:* finished
> *size:* 20 inch length, 14 inch waist

Old Sturbridge Village
26.40.24

BABY'S SHIRT

Worn by Samuel P. Kidder of Derryfield, New Hampshire, in 1768.
Plain weave.

  warp: undyed single Z-twist linen, 60 per inch
  weft: undyed single Z-twist linen, 54 per inch
  size: 8 1/2 x 18 1/4 inches

Manchester Historic Association
6126

SHIRT

Worn in the Davis family of North Andover, Massachusetts. 'J B Davis 8' written in ink in lower left corner. Plain weave.

> *warp:* bleached single Z-twist linen, 126 per inch
> *weft:* bleached single Z-twist linen, 128 per inch
> *edges:* finished
> *size:* 38 inches long, 17 1/2 inches at shoulders

North Andover Historical Society
36.89

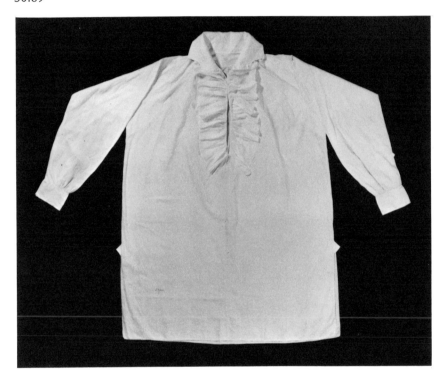

SHIFT

Made by E. Bradford. 'E. Bradford' written center bodice. Plain weave.

> *warp:* bleached single Z-twist linen, 98 per inch
> *weft:* bleached single Z-twist linen, 92 per inch
> *edges:* all finished
> *size:* 54 length, 26 waist

Old Sturbridge Village
26.26.16

APRON

Made by Elizabeth Dunham. Plain weave.

warp: undyed and blue single Z-twist linen, 40 per inch
weft: undyed and blue single Z-twist, 42 per inch
edges: two selvage, the rest hemmed
size: 51 x 51 1/2 inches when open full

Old Sturbridge Village
26.39.55

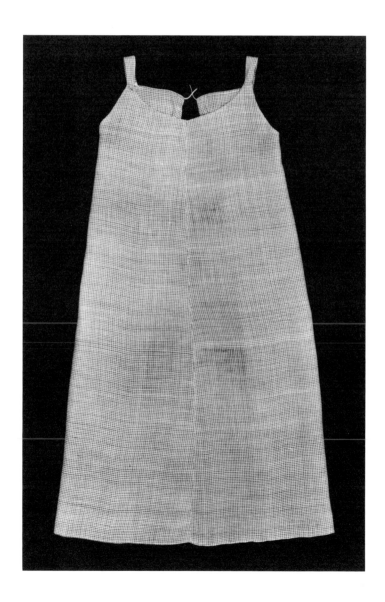

DECORATION

As the staple fiber of the preindustrial period, linen typically served as the background for decorative needle- and art-work. Pen and ink, inscriptions, lace and embroidery were all in vogue. Girls embroidered samplers in order to practice stitches which would later grace fancy garments. With industrialization, needlework became even more popular as middle-class women had more time to devote to leisure activities. Cotton replaced homespun linen for backing most needlework, but inventive Victorian women revived their ancestors' linen tablecloths and towels by adding colorful embroidery.

[Spelling book illustration, specimen book of Johnson & Smith, Philadelphia, 1834] reproduced in Clarence P. Hornung, *Handbook of Early American Advertising Art* (New York: Dover Publications, 1947) Wood engraving.

PILLOWCASE (detail)

Made at the Philbrick Farm, Weare, New Hampshire. Bobbin lace decoration (3/4 inch wide) of undyed two-ply S-twist linen. Plain weave.

> *warp:* undyed single Z-twist linen, 76 per inch
> *weft:* undyed single Z-twist linen, 66 per inch
> *edges:* one hemmed with bobbin lace decoration
> *size:* 38 3/4 x 21 inches

Society for the Preservation of New England Antiquities
1949.18B

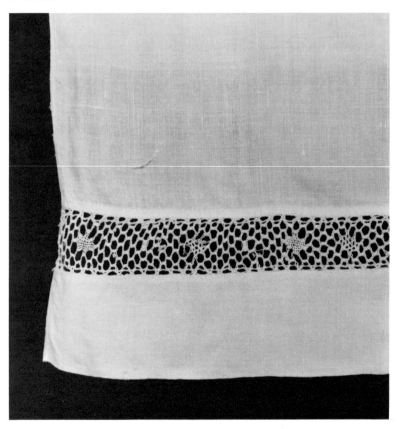

PILLOWCASE (detail)

Made by Martha Dunlap (1745-1812) of Bedford, New Hampshire. Bobbin lace in center panel (2 1/2 inches wide) of undyed two-ply linen S-twist; 'MD' cross-stitched in lower center. Plain weave.

> *warp:* undyed single Z-twist linen, 68 per inch
> *weft:* undyed single Z-twist linen, 64 per inch
> *edges:* one hemmed
> *size:* 30 3/4 x 15 3/4 inches

Currier Gallery of Art
P.C.D. 2a (270)

PILLOWCASE   (detail)

Made by Sarah Gordon of Bedford, New Hampshire. Plain weave.
'1821/Sarah Gordon' and a poem by Reed all written in ink in lower
right corner.

> Sarah, may angels guard thy bed,
> And hover o'er thy pillow'd head,
> May heaven, all kind, omnipotent and wise
> Appoint some seraph from his blissful skies
> To guard thee over with a tender care
> And of all blessings mayest thou have a share.
>   *Reed*

warp: undyed single Z-twist linen, 60 per inch
weft: undyed single Z-twist linen, 60 per inch
edges: one hemmed
size: 34 3/4 x 17 3/4 inches

New Hampshire Historical Society
1967.27.3B

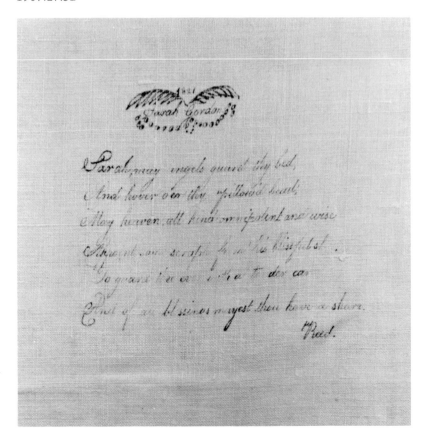

TABLECLOTH

Made by Nancy Farthingham Howlett or Elizabeth Petty Howlett about 1800 in Massachusetts. Embroidered with silk about 1894 by Angeline Shaw Mower Howlett of Cambridge, Massachusetts. M's and O's and point twill weave, eight-harness.

> warp: undyed single Z-twist linen, 42 per inch
> weft: undyed single Z-twist linen, 58 per inch
> edges: four fringed (2 inch)
> size: 16 1/2 x 17 inches
> repeat: 2 x 2 inches

Merrimack Valley Textile Museum
76.17

111

PETTICOAT

ca. 1766? Linen embroidery: light blue and dark blue singles Z-twist.
Plain weave.

- *warp:* undyed single Z-twist linen, 56 per inch
- *weft:* undyed single Z-twist linen, 48 per inch
- *edges:* bottom edge bound with wool twill tape, top edge raw, sewn into a tube
- *size:* 88 1/2 inches around, 37 inches length

Currier Gallery of Art
P.C.B. 3 (282)

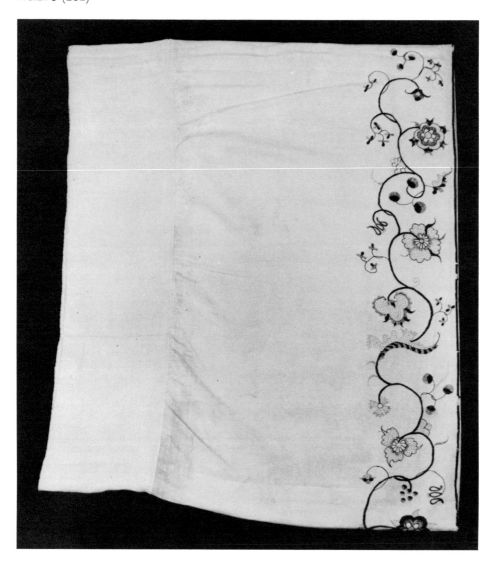

VEST FRONTS

Worn by John Marden for his marriage in 1769 at Derryfield, New Hampshire. Wool embroidery (pink, yellow, light blue, dark blue, brown, white). Plain weave.

> *warp:* undyed single Z-twist linen, 34 per inch
> *weft:* undyed single Z-twist cotton, 40 per inch
> *edges:* hemmed and raw
> *size:* 32 x 31 inches

Manchester Historic Association
3642-3

SAMPLER

Made in 1822 by Sarah Prescott Lawrence (1813-?) of Westford,
Massachusetts. Silk embroidery; cross-stitched with french knots.
Plain weave.

warp:	undyed single Z-twist linen, 30 per inch
weft:	undyed single Z-twist linen, 32 per inch
edges:	one selvage, three turned under
size:	12 3/8 x 12 1/4 inches

Essex Institute
122,669

SAMPLER

Made by Sarah Todd (1793-?) of Salem, Massachusetts, in 1807. Silk embroidery. Plain weave.

  warp: undyed single Z-twist linen, 28 per inch
  weft: undyed single Z-twist linen, 36 per inch
  edges: all turned under
  size: 26 x 25 1/2 inches

Essex Institute
133,992

BIBLIOGRAPHIC ESSAY

Because "Linen-making in New England" encompasses the interests of the horticulturalist, the craftsperson, and the historian, and because no single work examines linen comprehensively in its historical context, a researcher must consult a long and diverse list of sources to learn about the topic. This bibliography will point out the most useful of these sources, without attempting to be comprehensive.

The properties of flax as a fiber and of linen cloth as compared to other fabrics are touched upon in William H. Dooley, *Textiles for Commercial, Industrial, Evening, and Domestic Arts Schools* (Boston, 1910), Perry Walton, *The Story of Textiles* (New York, 1925), and Michael M. Bogle, *Technical Data on Linen*, Textile Conservation Notes #4 (North Andover, Mass., 1979). John Wily, *A Treatise on the Propagation of Sheep, the Manufacture of Wool, and the Cultivation and Manufacture of Flax* (Williamsburg, Va., 1765) and volume 15 of Abraham Rees, *The Cyclopaedia* (Philadelphia, 1822), provide complete advice on cultivating and processing flax, while the U.S. Department of Agriculture, *A Report on Flax, Hemp, Ramie and Jute* (Washington, D.C., 1890) covers the same subject from the point of view of late-nineteenth-century scientific agriculture. Simple descriptions of the processing of flax appear in Alice Morse Earle, *Home Life in Colonial Days* (New York, 1900), two articles on flax and linen by W.T. Charley in G. Philips Bevan, ed., *British Manufacturing Industries* (London, 1876) and H.R. Carter, *Flax and Its Products* (London, 1929). The latter deals with the modern period in Europe, but contains detailed information about the processing of flax before mechanization was extensive. Historical developments in linen technology before industrialization are documented in G.B. Thompson, *Spinning Wheels (The John Horner Collection)*, Ulster Museum Bulletin, vol. 1 (1952), reprint ed. (1964); David A. Pennington and Michael B. Taylor, *A Pictorial Guide to American Spinning Wheels* (Sabbathday Lake, Maine, 1975); and Dorothy K. MacDonald, *Fibres, Spindles, and Spinning-Wheels* (Toronto, 1950); and the issue of *CIBA Review* vol. 28, (December, 1939) which contains several articles on spinning wheels.

There are many good surveys of European and American economic history which either focus or touch upon linen. The best book on linen in Europe is John Horner, *The Linen Trade of Europe During the Spinning Wheel Period* (Belfast, Ireland, 1920), while Alfred S. Moore, *Linen*, (New York, 1900) and William F. Leggett, *The Story of Linen* (New York, 1945) cover the same topic in less detail. Conrad Gill, *The Rise of the Irish Linen Industry* (1925), reprint ed. (Oxford, 1964) and Horner can be supplemented with the Ulster Folk and Transport Museum, *Illustrations of the Irish Linen Industry in 1783 by William Hincks* (Newry, Ireland, 1977) for an understanding of the special Irish case.

William R. Bagnall, *The Textile Industries of the United States Including Sketches and Notices of Cotton, Woolen, Silk and Linen Manufactures in the Colonial Period,* vol. 1 (1639-1810), (Cambridge, Mass., 1893) is largely successful in accomplishing what its title claims for it; Bagnall reviewed local primary sources and legislation thoroughly. J. Leander Bishop, *A History of American Manufactures,* vol. 1 (1608-1860), (Philadelphia, 1864) and Victor S. Clark, *History of Manufactures in the United States,* vol. 1 (1607-1860), (1929), reprint ed. (New York, 1949) are similarly detailed compendia, especially useful on the early factory system. With its examination of the Boston linen manufactory, Gary B. Nash, "The Failure of Female Factory Labor in Colonial Boston," *Labor History* (Spring 1979) will interest those concerned with linen as well as historians studying the workers who made linen. Three well-researched economic histories, Rolla Milton Tryon, *Household Manufactures in the United States, 1640-1860* (Chicago, 1917), William B. Weeden, *Economic and Social History of New England, 1620-1789* (Boston, 1890) and Howard S. Russell, *A Long Deep Furrow: Three Centuries of Farming in New England* (Hanover, N.H., 1976) are invaluable, documenting the scope and depth of the linen industry in America. Vol. 3, *Manufactures*, of the *Eighth Census of the United States: 1860*, includes a short, useful survey of the industry's history, while Nathaniel B. Shurtleff, ed., *Records of the Governor and Company of the Massachusetts Bay in New England,* 5 vols. (Boston, 1853-54) includes the relevant colonial legislation in the Commonwealth.

Special censuses and reports compiled by advocates of American manufacturing are especially useful for tracing the contours of household industry before and during its decline. *American State Papers*, (1832), vol. 4, *Finances*, contains two reports made several years earlier: Albert Gallatin's "Manufactures" (#325) was researched in 1810, and Tench Coxe's "Digest of Manufactures," (#407) dates from 1814. Tench Coxe also carried out statistical and verbal surveys of manufacturing, including linen. These were published as *A Statement of the Arts and Manufactures of the United States* and *A Series of Tables of the Several Branches of American Manufactures* in the Census of 1810, reprinted in 1970 in *American Industry and Manufactures in the Nineteenth Century: a Basic Source Collection*, vol. 2 (Elmsford, New York, 1970). Louis McLane, *Documents Relative to the Manufactures in the United States*, 2 vols. (1833), reprint ed. (New York, 1969) includes valuable questionnaires on the state of the industry in 1824 and also comments by observers of the time.

The story of the Scotch-Irish emigration to New England can be found in a few modern monographs, in nineteenth-century local histories, and in the partisan accounts of the descendants of the emigrants. The best book on the ethnic group's experience in Europe is R.J. Dickson, *Ulster Emigration to Colonial America 1718-1775* (London, 1966) while James G. Leyburn, *The Scotch-Irish: a Social History* (Chapel Hill, 1962) moves into a well-researched account of their emigration and their experience in America. Gordon Woodbury, "The Scotch-Irish and Irish Presbyterian Settlers of New Hampshire" in *Proceedings* of the New Hampshire Historical Society 4 (1899-1905), and Robert C. Mack, *Exercises on the One-Hundred-Fiftieth Anniversary of the Settlement of Old Nutfield* (Manchester, N.H., 1870) covers the same tale in the less objective fashion of the turn of the century. Rev. Edward L. Parker, *History of Londonderry* (Boston, 1851) along with George Waldo Browne, ed., *Early Records of Londonderry, Windham and Derry, New Hampshire, 1719-62* (Manchester, N.H., 1908) are essential for the study of the Scotch-Irish and can be supplemented with Jeremy Belknap, *The History of New-Hampshire*, vol. 2 (Boston, 1791) and vol. 3 (Boston, 1792) and John McClintock, *History of New Hampshire* (Boston, 1889). Samuel G. Drake, *The History and Antiquities of Boston* (Boston, 1856) refers to the arrival of the Scotch-Irish before they moved on to Londonderry. There are histories of many towns and counties settled by emigrants from Londonderry, including *The History of*

Bedford (Concord, N.H., 1903); Benjamin Chase, *History of Old Chester* (Auburn, N.Y., 1869); Rev. W.R. Cochrane, *History of the Town of Antrim, New Hampshire* (Manchester, 1880); D. Hamilton Hurd, ed., *History of Rockingham and Strafford Counties, New Hampshire* (Philadelphia, 1882); Leonard A. Morrison, *The History of Windham in New Hampshire* (Boston, 1883) and *Supplement to the History of Windham in New Hampshire* (Boston, 1892); Albert Smith, *History of the Town of Peterborough* (Boston, 1876) and Joseph Williamson, *History of the City of Belfast in the State of Maine* (Portland, Me., 1877). In some cases these contain useful genealogical information on Scotch-Irish individuals such as weavers, or provide details of the linen industry in that locale.

In addition to these local histories, manuscript sources, published or unpublished, are available. An excellent diary is that of Matthew Patten of Bedford, New Hampshire, published by the Town of Bedford in 1903. Patten, a farmer, lawyer and local official descended from the Londonderry Scotch-Irish, kept clear account of his transactions related to linen. The diary of John Campbell, a Scotch-Irish farmer of Windham, New Hampshire, is held at the New Hampshire Historical Society archives. Collections of probate inventories, which catalogue possessions in an estate at the time of death, reveal how widely linens and flax-processing equipment were owned. These are generally stored in county probate offices, but the New Hampshire Historical Society has a statewide collection for the years up to about 1770 on microfilm, and the collection edited by Abbott Cummings, *Rural Household Inventories 1675-1775* (Boston, 1964) is very useful. The account books of general stores, weavers and farmers are essential for tracing patterns of trade, and can be found in many general archives. George Francis Dow, *The Arts and Crafts in New England, 1704-1775* (Topsfield, Mass., 1927) reprints advertisements and articles from colonial Boston newspapers, including groups on fabrics and trades. Travel accounts which mention the industry include the annotations made in 1787 by George Grieve to Francois-Jean, Marquis de Chastellux, *Travels in North America in the Years 1780, 1781, and 1782*, found in revised translation by Howard C. Rice, Jr. (Chapel Hill, 1963); *Some Cursory Remarks Made by James Birkit in His Voyage to North America, 1750-51*, Yale Historical Manuscripts (New Haven, 1916); and David John Jeremy, *Henry*

Wansey and his American Journal (Philadelphia, 1970). The *New England Farmer* periodically printed articles on flax early in the nineteenth century.

Sources on industrial linen-making are thin, both for technological and economic information. The place to begin is again the essay on linen in vol. 3 of the 1860 census, which outlines the reasons for linen's failure to compete with cotton. *Water Power and its Application to Flax Scutching in Ulster*, an undated pamphlet published by the Ulster Museum, gives an excellent technical and historical sketch of early scutching mills. Orra L. Stone, *History of Massachusetts Industries* (Boston, 1930), summarizes the histories of the most important linen factories and should be supplemented with the censuses of population and of manufacturing in Massachusetts, published by the state Bureau of Labor Statistics. These censuses tally each factory operating in the state, noting the sex, ages and wages of the employees. Charlotte Erickson, *Invisible Immigrants: The Adaptation of English and Scottish Immigrants in Nineteenth-Century America* (Coral Gables, Florida, 1972) is a collection of immigrants' letters which includes a series written by a Scottish flax hackler working in the early mills of Massachusetts. Although it is based on a shop-floor study of Irish linen millworkers in the early twentieth century, Betty Messenger, *Picking Up the Linen Threads: a Study in Industrial Folklore* (Austin, Texas, 1978) records songs, rhymes and first-hand observations which illuminate life in the American factories as well. For the comparison with the cotton industry, see Caroline Ware's classic history, *The Early New England Cotton Manufacture: a Study in Industrial Beginnings* (Boston, 1931).